AN
ECONOMIC GEOGRAPHY
OF OIL

BELL'S ECONOMIC GEOGRAPHIES

General Editor
PROFESSOR R. O. BUCHANAN
M.A.(N.Z.), B.Sc.(Econ.), Ph.D.(London)
Professor Emeritus, University of London

In Preparation

ECONOMICS AND GEOGRAPHY
Michael Chisholm, M.A.

AGRICULTURAL GEOGRAPHY
Leslie Symons, B.Sc.(Econ.), Ph.D.

PLANTATION AGRICULTURE
Philip P. Courtenay, B.A., Ph.D.

GREATER LONDON: AN INDUSTRIAL GEOGRAPHY
J. E. Martin, B.Sc.(Econ.), Ph.D.

AN
ECONOMIC GEOGRAPHY
OF OIL

PETER R. ODELL
B.A., Ph.D.

Lecturer in Geography,
London School of Economics and Political Science

LONDON

G. BELL AND SONS, LTD

1963

First published 1963

Printed in Great Britain by
NEILL & CO. LTD., EDINBURGH

Preface

This short book aims to present an analysis of the distribution of the activities of the world oil industry. In making this attempt I am conscious of the magnitude of the task, which arises not only from the size and complexity of the operations involved in getting over 1000 million tons of oil a year out of the ground and through the various stages of manufacture and transport to the consumers throughout the world, but also from the diversity of the industry's organizational structure ranging from the vast internationally integrated private enterprise companies, to the state-owned undertakings of the communist countries and of various other countries of the world and to the large number of small companies, some involved in all aspects of oil operations from exploration to marketing, but many more involved in only a single aspect of the industry. Limitations on space present one handicap to my doing full justice to the subject but of much greater significance in this respect is my own inability to grasp and to bring out all the relevant factors which contribute to the geographical distribution of the production, refining and consumption of oil.

It seems, therefore, that my temerity in writing this book needs some justification. Essentially I would argue the need for an introductory study of the distribution of oil industry activities. While the developments and changes are reported and analyzed extensively in a plethora of technical and trade journals and governmental and intergovernmental reports, nevertheless the industry has not been the subject of a great deal of basic geographical analysis on a world basis. It is this gap which the book seeks partly to fill.

If I have succeeded in this task to even a limited degree, the book may be useful to those students and teachers who are participating in the rapid growth of the study of economic geography. I also hope that students of other disciplines engaged in their own analyses of the oil industry and those people officially or professionally concerned with oil affairs may find this to be a useful introductory volume. Those laymen who are interested in an industry which increasingly makes 'the world's wheels go round' may too find it of some interest.

There are two points which I feel need to be made clear concerning the book. Firstly, it does not provide explanations —except in passing—of the techniques of oil exploration, production and refining. Background knowledge of these is assumed but those readers who feel they lack this are referred to the relevant chapters in *The World Geography of Petroleum* (American Geographical Society Publication No. 31, edited by W. A. Pratt and D. Good), or to those in the *Petroleum Handbook* (published by Shell International Petroleum Co. Ltd) or to appropriate publications of the Petroleum Information Bureau in London.

Secondly, the book by and large is not concerned with the domestic oil industry of the United States. Had it been included then, by virtue of its size relative to the industry in the rest of the world, it would necessarily have taken up too much of the available space. Moreover, since the Second World War the United States oil industry and that in the rest of the non-communist world have essentially pursued their own separate patterns of development. References to the United States oil industry, therefore, are generally restricted to bringing out the important points of contact between it and the industry in the rest of the world and to offering United States experience as a guide to possible future developments in other parts of the world.

Many people have helped me in the preparation of this book and I gratefully acknowledge their assistance. There are several to whom I am indebted for a great deal of help. Professor R. O. Buchanan, the editor of this new series of economic geographies, has generously given his advice and encouragement. Dr. E. T. Penrose, Reader in Economics at the London School of Economics, Mr. S. Cody of the Public Relations Department of Iranian Oil Services Ltd, and Mr. J. G. Trimmer, Head of the Economics Division of Shell International Petroleum Co. Ltd, and his colleagues in the

Division, notably Dr. H. DuMoulin, have all read the text in draft and gave much of their time in constructively criticizing my presentation and my arguments and in offering suggestions for improving the work. The book has been made much more accurate and readable as a result of their efforts and I am deeply grateful to them. However, for the shortcomings and in-accuracies which remain and for the particular viewpoints—some perhaps controversial—which the book expresses I do, of course, take full responsibility. Finally, I would acknowledge my debt to Mrs. E. Wilson and Miss E. E. Woodhams for drawing the maps and diagrams often with nothing more than a page or two of statistics and a few of my vague ideas from which to work.

P.R.O.

London School of Economics
September 1962

Contents

ix

Maps and Diagrams

List of Tables

PART I

THE PATTERN
OF
WORLD OIL SUPPLY

CHAPTER 1

The Industry's Resource Base

The generally accepted theory of the process of oil formation implies the existence of a finite quantity of oil available for mankind's use and the spectre of the exhaustion of reserves has often been raised. It is estimated that by the end of 1961 some 18,000 million tons of oil had been used since the industry started about a century earlier. Of this total amount, however, almost 50 per cent. was consumed in the decade 1950–60 when the rate of consumption increased very rapidly in most parts of the world. The 1960 consumption of over 1000 million tons has been compared with the figure for proven reserves of oil which stand at little more than 40,000 million tons. This relationship between current production and proven reserves apparently seems to indicate a future for the industry of only forty years and much less than this if consumption continues to expand at the current rate of about 7 per cent. per annum. It is largely on the basis of this comparison that the charge is laid that the world is running out of oil, which should not, therefore, be relied upon to provide energy for the future. For example, Mr. W. Wyatt, the Member of Parliament for a constituency which includes the greater part of the Leicester-shire coalfield, in a speech in the House of Commons on Britain's energy position in 1959, commented:

'How safe will it be to reduce our coal consumption. . . . It may be 30 years before atomic energy can be relied upon to provide any substantial load of power. Meanwhile, oil is running out fast. . . . The consumption of oil in the world is going up by 7% a year. . . . In 20 years there will almost certainly be a major crisis in the world. The proved reserves today are only 40,000 million tons and even the wildest estimates of future discoveries do not put the total amount of oil in the world at more than 200,000 million tons. A good deal of that is in areas which it is extremely difficult to drill and exploit.

3

In 20 years time the oil companies will be down to about the last 30 years of their supply at the rate of consumption which will then have been reached in the world as a whole.' [1]

In March, 1961, the economic adviser to the National Coal Board, Mr. E. F. Schumacher, expressed the belief that it is 'completely uncertain' whether sufficient oil will be available to supply Britain's energy requirements in the 1980s.[2]

Is the resource base of the oil industry as narrow as these observations suggest? If so then it seems likely that the general world-wide preference for liquid over solid fuels will be foiled by a physical shortage of oil supplies in the later part of the twentieth century. The answer is not to be found in a comparison of production trends with the figures for proven reserves, for the latter represent only the 'working inventory' of the industry and do not give any indication of the quantity of oil available for future use. Proven reserves is a concept concerned only with those pools of oil in the ground which are known to exist as a result of actual drilling operations and from which a certain proportion (varying from field to field depending on local conditions) of the oil in place can be recovered by known production systems at the contemporary level of costs and prices.

The reserves are proven by exploration drilling and by drilling to delimit the extent of the oil-bearing formations in areas in which oil has been discovered. Such exploration and development is not carried out by companies merely for the sake of proving the underground existence of oil but in order that they can locate supplies of oil to meet their future requirements.* But their future requirements are assessed by reference to current consumption: thus exploration—and hence the level of proven reserves—are a function of demand.

This is clearly brought out in an examination of the relationship between production (which, as shown in Chapter 4, may be roughly equated with demand) and proven reserves. World production of oil in 1938 was under 250 million tons and proven reserves were then a little more than 4000 million tons. By 1960 production had increased four times to over 1000 million tons but proven reserves stood ten times higher at over 40,000

---

* Although in Venezuela it seems likely that legislation may be enacted shortly to require oil companies to 'prove' the whole of their concession areas, only one-eighth of which at the moment have been drilled.

million tons, even though in the intervening twenty-two years no less than 12,000 million tons of oil had been produced— three times as much as the proven reserves of the earlier date. Over the shorter period 1950–60 production doubled and proven reserves increased threefold, even though during these ten years production equivalent to about 40 per cent. of the proven reserves of 1950 was consumed. In fact, in every year in the post-war period the annual production of oil has been exceeded by the increase in the amount of proven reserves. Between 1958 and 1959, for example, production increased by about 70 million tons; proven reserves in that year increased by 1570 million tons.

TABLE 1

DISTRIBUTION OF
WORLD PROVEN CRUDE OIL RESERVES, 1961

(in millions of metric tons)

Middle East	25,600
North America	6,100
Soviet Sphere	4,575
South America	3,175
Far East	1,400
North Africa	700
Rest of World	825
Total	42,375

Source: Based on B.P. Statistical Review of the World Oil Industry 1961

Figures of proven reserves—perhaps given unfortunate and misleading emphasis even by the oil industry—can thus be discounted in an assessment of the resource base. The distribution of these proven reserves at the end of 1961, shown in Table 1, is little more than an indication of the immediate productive capacity in various parts of the world. It has been observed that 'their location and quantity varies by and large in accordance with the direction, intensity and skill of discovery work',[3] and does not indicate the distribution of oil resources. The distribution of proven reserves is, of course, constantly changing as new discoveries are made, resources are withdrawn from established fields and new assessments are made of the

B

oil in place and the likely recovery possibilities. The magnitude of the changes is seen in the growth of Middle East proven reserves from only 700 million tons in 1938 to over 25,000 million tons in 1961 during which period its share of the world total increased from 17 per cent. to over 60 per cent.

Having thus discounted the value of proven reserves for indicating the magnitude of the industry's resource base, it is necessary to study the assessments that have been made of the amount of oil in place in the earth's surface and to consider the possibilities of extracting it. The attempt to put a figure on the world's ultimate recoverable reserves has been described as an 'essentially speculative subject' [4] and we are also warned by one of the world's leading authorities in this field that the figure should not be looked on 'with anything like the same confidence as proved reserves'.[5] Even in the United States, where the petroleum geologists have made more extensive and intensive studies than elsewhere in the world, there have been many estimates of the country's oil producing potential.[6] Thus, on a world wide basis the estimates can be of only the roughest kind, for the exercise involves the assessment of vast areas of sedimentary basins which have never been drilled and the geology of many of which is little known.

In spite of the uncertainty, however, the possibilities appear to be very large, for 18 million of the world's 22 million square miles of sedimentary basins—the distribution of which is illustrated in Figure 1—are considered to be effective basin areas from the point of view of oil potential. Only about 1 per cent. of these areas have been effectively explored for oil.[7] The sedimentary areas have been examined 'basin by basin' by L. G. Weeks with 'a careful study of each basin's geology over a long period'. He has assessed the likelihood of oil occurrence by reference to the geological facts of deposition, potential reservoir porosity, relative location of potential source and potential reservoir rocks and the existence of 'timely and adequate traps'.[8] From his studies he has conservatively assessed that the total world ultimate potential of liquid petroleum resources recoverable by conventional primary methods in terms of current economics is of the order of 300,000 million tons—enough for almost 300 years at the current rate of consumption.

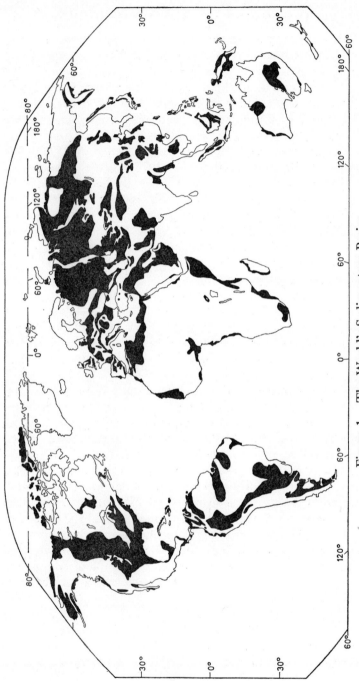

Figure 1. The World's Sedimentary Basins

This estimate, moreover, ignores the possibilities of using secondary methods of recovery (which will be examined later) and of the prospects of winning oil from greater depths. To date 85 per cent. of all the oil produced has come from depths of 2000–8000 feet, but it is 'expected that the deeper picture will improve with time as more and more deeper wildcats are drilled'.[9] This process of deeper drilling is now proceeding and the deepest production is from a depth of 25,000 feet compared with only 7500 feet in 1927. Little is known of the deepest possibilities but it is generally believed that 'the condition of the potential reservoir rocks rather than the breakdown of oil may be the limiting factors. There may be no single figure applicable to all areas, for the critical depth probably depends on the original characteristics of the rock and the setting, including the nature of the cover and the temperature gradients in that cover'.[10] Theoretically, oil may occur in sandstones down to a depth of 65,620 feet and in limestones to 51,300 feet.[11] Present exploration has hardly scratched the surface of the possibilities in depth. Technological progress in prospecting and in drilling seems certain to ensure that the theoretical limit will be more nearly approached in the future.

New areas of exploration are continually being sought and developed. The Sahara region provided a significant development in the late 1950s and major discoveries are still being made (see page 25). At the present time there appear to be particularly good prospects in the U.S.S.R. where there are indications of an oil area in Siberia, covering about 400,000 square miles and probably containing larger reserves than those of the Volga–Urals fields, which currently supply almost three-quarters of the country's total production. The Canadian Arctic Islands are also thought to offer favourable prospects, for exploration permits covering 43 million acres have been taken up by twenty-two companies or groups of companies. An editorial in a Canadian oil journal described the prospects in the following terms:

'Sediments thousands of feet thick; structures rivalling in size those of the Middle East; reservoir rocks with porosity and permeability undreamed of in Western Canada; the hope of gushers like Spindletop. The dream of a 100,000 barrels per day (about 5 million tons per year) from a single well. The prospect of 50,000 million barrels (7000 million tons) of oil or more. More oil than the known reserves of Canada and the United States combined.' [12]

The Canadian Government commissioned an enquiry into the potentialities of the Arctic Islands and adjacent areas of the mainland. The report [13] confirms the physical possibilities of oil production on the large scale enthusiastically foreseen in the editorial quoted. There are also indications of new and important basins in parts of the Middle East from which oil is not currently produced. The Trucial Oman coast, for example, holds promise of becoming a major producing area, with particular and immediate attention on the Sheikdom of Abu Dhabi, where the success of exploration efforts in 1961 and early 1962 have already led to the area being described as a second Kuwait.

If, however, the likelihood of the continued discovery of new fields is entirely discounted, the physical possibilities for oil production are still not limited to the proven reserves. On average, the figure for proven reserves assumes a recovery rate of the oil in place which can be commercially produced at present costs and prices of only 33 per cent. Thus in the known fields, there is as much as 100,000 million tons of oil awaiting exploitation by means of improved recovery technology. A 1 per cent. improvement in the overall recovery efficiency from these fields would produce the equivalent of almost two years' supply at current rates.[14] Through the development of methods of secondary recovery in which water or gas is injected under pressure into the oil-pool, or by means of underground combustion (known as fireflooding), major improvements in recovery rates are assured.

In the United States, where the average primary recovery efficiency is about 35 per cent., and where secondary methods are now being applied more extensively and systematically, it is estimated that the recovery rate will be increased to 60 per cent. In the rest of the world (outside the Soviet Union) much less progress has been made in the application of secondary methods and it is 'not yet possible to build up a world picture with any pretensions to accuracy'.[15] Projects in different parts of the world suggest, however, that the United States' experience may be repeated on a world-wide scale. The Pembina field in Canada with an estimated 600 million tons of oil in place and a primary recovery of only 12·5 per cent. could be made to yield an additional 225 million tons of oil with the injection at high pressure of heavier gas fractions. Less ambitious secondary methods such as simple gas injection or waterflooding would at least double the recovery rate to give an additional minimum ultimate output from the field of 75 million tons. In Venezuela, in both the Eastern and the Maracaibo fields, the application of secondary recovery methods has increased the recovery rate by up to 14 per cent. In the Middle East, which is only now becoming an active area for secondary recovery operations, there have been comparable developments. In the Abquaiq field in Saudi Arabia it is estimated that secondary recovery methods will lift the percentage recovery from 35 to 70. On the basis of the evidence accumulated to date, it is estimated that even the relatively small number of secondary recovery projects will lead to an additional 11,000 million tons of oil becoming available.[16] The trend in recovery efficiency is thus 'strongly upwards' and this alone would seem to ensure an adequate supply of oil for the world for much of the remainder of the century. The application of secondary recovery methods to Week's estimate of total oil in place raises the ultimate level of recoverable resources from 300,000 million to 525,000 million tons.

This, however, does not exhaust the physical possibilities of producing oil for there are other sources which have not yet been touched. These are the very widespread occurrences of oil shales and tar sands known to exist in many parts of the world. Given the present level of technology and the present price levels for crude oil, these are uneconomic to work, but, in many cases, only a little more than marginally so, such that a small improvement in technology or a slight rise in the price level will make oil extraction from the shales and sands possible. In the United States it is estimated that there are 220,000 million tons of oil in shales with an oil content of 10 gallons or more per ton of shale. Canada also has large shale reserves and in addition has some 80,000 million tons of oil contained in the Athabasca tar sands of Alberta. Week estimates that in the world as a whole, the shales and sands contain energy resources 'as great or greater than those of liquid petroleum'.[17]

Thus, ultimately recoverable reserves of oil from the known and likely resource base seem likely to be in excess of 1 million, million tons and thus ensure the ability of the world oil industry to meet the demands placed on it for at least the rest of the twentieth century without an undue increase in the costs of crude oil production which, it has been estimated,[18] are under £1 per ton in parts of the Middle East and a little more than an average of £2 per ton in Venezuela.* Opinions, such as those quoted on page 3, that the world is running out of oil would thus seem not to be well-founded.

It is in the light of this wide resource base that one must examine the possibility of physical limitations on the geographical distribution of the industry's productive capacity. In fact, it seems unlikely that any major oil producing area or country has reached its physical limits of production. Until recently, there has been a considerable body of opinion that in the United States production was approaching its maximum after almost a century of increasingly intensive exploration and extraction.[19] Such prognostications have in general been based on a mechanical extrapolation of statistics of production, proven reserves and recovery rates from field to field. A recent comprehensive and authoritative survey of the energy situation, has, however, challenged both the general thesis and the methods by which such conclusions were reached. The survey has come to the conclusion that the total domestic availability of crude oil in the United States in 1975 will be of the order of 850 million tons (compared with a current annual rate of production of 350 million tons) 'at no appreciable increase in constant dollar costs'.[20] It should be noted that this is not a judgement of what production will be in 1975, as this will depend on decisions concerning imports and the regulation of production—the main determinants of the degree of explora-

---

* It should, moreover, be emphasized that as these production costs represent only a small part of the final prices of petroleum products to consumers, even a large proportional increase would not necessarily affect retail prices very significantly. For example, consumers in Britain pay about £70 per ton for gasoline, £30 for kerosene, £20 for home heating oils and £10 for fuel oil. Thus, the prices paid by consumers are much more a function of royalty and other payments to governments in producing countries, of refining and transport costs and of sales taxes than they are of the costs of lifting the oil out of the ground.

tion and development efforts—in the whole of the intervening period. It is rather a 'judgement of what production could be, under constant costs, in the light of the resource position and foreseeable technological progress'.[21] This figure of availability for 1975 does not, moreover, include oil that would become available given a higher price level thus permitting exploitation of higher cost reserves. A continuation or an intensification of the present United States policy of restricting imports of crude oil and products and thus effectively isolating United States crude prices from those of the rest of the non-communist world, is likely to produce a situation in which more oil pools become commercially attractive. It would also produce a situation in which a start could be made in the use of the country's oil shale reserves which constitute 'an abundant potential domestic source of liquid fuels that is considerably larger than the estimated crude oil base'.[22]

Such an optimistic estimate of the physical possibilities for oil production in the United States is perhaps all the more remarkable in the light of the fact that nowhere else in the world has the potential for petroleum production been explored so thoroughly in the last 100 years, during which period the United States has produced more than 50 per cent. of the total cumulative world output. As early as 1940 one well had been drilled to every twelve square miles of sedimentary basins compared with one well to every 1100 miles in the rest of the world.[23] In view of the past performance and the still remaining potential of the United States, which certainly does not have any unique geological advantages, it seems most unlikely that any other significant parts of the sedimentary areas of the world can be written off as having reached or even as approaching their physical limits of oil production. Such hypothetical physical limits of production might thus be discarded as a determinant of the world pattern of petroleum extraction now and for much of the remainder of the century.

The pattern of production will depend rather on regional variations in the input of capital into more and deeper wells to achieve a higher rate of primary recovery; into research and equipment to improve the chances of secondary recovery; and into the technology and development of the extraction of liquid petroleum from the oil shales and the tar sands. Such regional variations in the application of capital will be in part a function of the physical factors of oil occurrence—such as the climate and associated disincentives to activity in certain regions; the size of reservoirs; and the depth of oil deposits—which obviously affect costs differentially. In greater part, however, they will depend on other considerations such as the location of the areas of potential production in relation to the main centres of consumption, the organization of the industry, the impact of the forces of political and economic nationalism and the internal and external effects of decisions based on a different set of priorities and motivations in the countries of the Soviet bloc. The impact of these factors will be examined in Chapter 3.

REFERENCES

1 *Hansard.* House of Commons. 23rd November 1959. Col. 101.

2 E. F. Schumacher. 'The Economic Approach to Heating in the Future.' A paper presented to the C.U.C.—N.C.B. Conference, Torquay, 24th March 1962.

3 D.C. Ion. 'Oil Resources in the Next Half Century.' A Paper presented to the Institute of Petroleum Summer Meeting, Torquay, June 1956.

4 D. C. Ion. *Ibid.*

5 L. G. Weeks. 'Fuel Reserves of the Future.' *Bulletin of the American Association of Petroleum Geologists.* Vol. 42, No. 2, February 1958, p. 434.

6 S. H. Schurr and B. C. Netschert. *Energy in the American Economy,* 1850–1975, pp. 347–389.

7 L. G. Weeks. *Op. cit.*

8 L. G. Weeks. *Ibid.*

9 G. M. Knebel and G. Rodriquez-Eraso. 'Habitat of some Oil.' *Bulletin of the American Association of Petroleum Geologists.* Vol. 40, No. 4, April 1956, p. 527.

10 G. D. Hobson. 'Why are oil reserves continually growing? Geological Considerations.' *Institute of Petroleum Review.* Vol. 15, No. 177, September 1961, p. 273.

11 J. S. Cloninger. 'How Deep Oil and Gas may be expected.' *World Oil.* Vol. 130, No. 6, May 1950, p. 60.

12 *Oilweek.* Editorial. 26th June, 1961.

13 G. David Quirin. *Economics of Oil and Gas Development in Northern Canada,* 1962.

14 M. Stephenson. 'The Potential of Secondary Recovery in increasing Oil Reserves.' *Institute of Petroleum Review.* Vol. 15, No. 179, November 1961.

15 M. Stephenson. *Ibid.*
16 M. Stephenson. *Ibid.*
17 L. G. Weeks. *Op. cit.*
18 International Bank for Reconstruction and Development. *The Economic Development of Venezuela.* 1961, p. 128.
19 See, for example, E. Ayres and C. A. Scarlott. *Energy Sources; the Wealth of the World.* 1952, pp. 29–47.
20 S. H. Schurr and B. C. Netschert. *Op. cit.*, p. 386.
21 S. H. Schurr and B. C. Netschert. *Ibid.*, p. 386.
22 S. H. Schurr and B. C. Netschert. *Ibid.*, p. 387.
23 W. E. Pratt. *Oil in the Earth.* 1942, p. 65.

CHAPTER 2

The World Pattern of Production

The total world output of crude oil exceeded 1000 million metric tons for the first time in 1960. Just one decade earlier production had exceeded 500 million tons for the first time so that in the 1950s the annual average increase in output was of the order of 7 per cent. In both 1960 and 1961 an additional 70 million tons was produced and by mid-1962 output was running at a level of over 1150 million tons. The world pattern of production in 1961 is illustrated in Figure 2.

The United States stands out clearly as the major petroleum producer with an output over twice as great as that of any other country. However, production in the United States is now practically stable at about 350 million tons and the annual increases in production since 1958 have been very small. This reflects the impact of schemes, first introduced in the early 1930s, for restricting oil production. The major objective of these prorationing schemes has been the maintenance of crude oil prices.[1] Partly as a result of them, increasing imports of both crude oil and oil products have been attracted into the country and United States oil has, moreover, been priced out of the world market except for highly specialized products and for purchases of oil made by the United States military authorities for their forces overseas. Additionally, for reasons which will be examined later (see pages 81–85), there has recently been a much slower rate of increase in the demand for petroleum and this has also adversely affected production. Thus, United States production is well below capacity in all of the major producing regions. For example in Texas, which accounts for about one-third of total output, there is an effective system of restricting output in force. In 1961 only the equivalent of 104 days' output was allowed from each well. This was the lowest figure since the system of prorationing

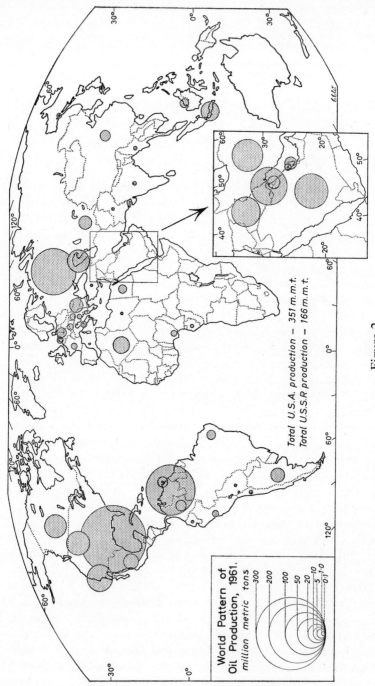

World Pattern of
Oil Production, 1961.
million metric tons

Total U.S.A. production — 351 m.m.t.
Total U.S.S.R production — 166 m.m.t.

Figure 2

began and was much less than the 'daily allowables' for recent years (126 for 1959, 122 in 1958 and 161 in 1957). An indication of the declining relative importance of the United States in the world picture of petroleum production is shown by the fact that it now produces little more than one-third of the world total; in 1950 its share was more than 50 per cent.; and in 1940 it accounted for almost two-thirds.

The development of Canadian resources contrasts significantly with the long standing importance of the oil industry in the United States. Canadian production is essentially a phenomenon of the last decade. Production in 1945 was only 1·2 million tons. This increased to 4 million tons by 1950, following the major discovery of the Leduc field in 1947, but there then ensued an oil boom of large proportions which raised output to 18 million tons in 1955 and to 25 million in 1957. Since then the boom conditions have faded and it was not until 1961 that there was another significant increase in output (to 31 million tons). It is estimated that about half of western Canada's oil producing capacity was idle in 1961 under the impact of unfavourable marketing conditions arising from a deceleration in the rate of increase in Canadian demand and from competition in eastern Canada from imported oil, which can now be landed at highly competitive prices because of the combination of weak world crude oil price levels and low tanker freight rates. The under-utilization of the available oil resources led to detailed government enquiries into the situation and, as a result of these, the government has set targets for the industry such that production is to be raised to 40 million tons in 1963. The 5 million ton jump in output in 1961 is partly a result of this state intervention in the affairs of the industry, but further significant developments are needed if the targets are to be met. It will necessitate, for example, increased exports to the United States which, as we have just seen, has under-utilized capacity of its own and where some sectors of the industry are seeking a curb on imports from Canada to match those on imports from every other country (except Mexico). It will also involve Canadian oil replacing imported oil from markets in Eastern Ontario and Quebec— a development which will necessitate the construction of a pipeline from Alberta to Montreal. If there is continued weakness in world oil prices, the replacement of foreign oil by domestic supplies may well be achieved only by the imposition of mandatory controls on imports by the Canadian government.

The U.S.S.R. is now the world's second largest producer and is certain to remain so for the rest of the decade, when its output will be approaching that of the United States. The Soviet Union moved into second place only in 1961, when its production of 166 million tons exceeded production in Venezuela for the first time. The rapid growth of the Soviet oil industry will be examined in more detail in Chapter 3, but it may be briefly noted at this stage that production almost doubled in the period 1950–55, and then more than doubled between 1955 and 1960. This was largely as a result of the expansion of output from the new fields of the Volga–Urals region. Production from the old established fields of the Caucasus has risen little above its pre-war level of 30 million tons per annum in spite of the development of off-shore facilities in the Caspian Sea.[2]

Venezuela is the world's third producer and, in contrast to both the United States and the Soviet Union, it produces primarily for export. Of the total production of 151 million tons in 1961, only 6 million were consumed domestically (including the consumption of the large refineries). Production in Venezuela started in 1921 and by the outbreak of the Second World War had risen to almost 30 million tons a year. Production in the early years of the war varied as a result of German submarine activity but once this menace had been overcome output rose rapidly under the impact of greatly increased investment by United States companies which by 1945 accounted for over 70 per cent. of total output (50·5 per cent. in 1939).[3] The rapid rate of growth persisted until 1957, when, as a result of the Suez crisis, which reduced supplies for Europe from the Middle East, total output exceeded 145 million tons. Production fell back in 1958 as Europe reverted to restored supplies from the Middle East, and since then Venezuelan production has grown at a much slower rate under the impact of generally unfavourable political and economic conditions.

Venezuela has until recently dominated oil production in Latin America. Outside Venezuela, production in Latin

America was less than 20 million tons until 1950.   At that time Mexico accounted for about 50 per cent. and Colombia for another 25 per cent. of this amount.   Since 1950, however, and more particularly since 1953, Latin American production has increased rapidly and by 1961 had reached a level of more than 50 million tons, of which Mexico contributed 15 million, Argentina 12·5 million, Colombia 7·5, Trinidad 6·6 and Brazil 4·7 million tons.   Until 1957, Venezuela's production increased sufficiently rapidly to increase its share of the Latin American total to 84 per cent. (compared with 78 per cent. in 1950).   By 1961, however, its share had fallen to a little over 75 per cent. and this trend may be expected to continue over at least the next few years.

The Middle East as a whole is the world's major producing region outside the United States but, as shown in Figure 2, output is divided among several different states, four of which produced more than 50 million tons each in 1961.   Kuwait, a state smaller than Wales, produced about 83 million tons and was followed in order of importance by Saudi Arabia (68·5 million tons), Iran (58·8 million tons), and Iraq (50 million tons).   The changing significance of the various producing countries in the Middle East is brought out in Figure 3, which shows the pattern of production in the period since 1946.   This clearly brings out the major changes that have taken place (within the overall pattern of a rapidly increasing output from the area as a whole) under the impact of the development of new facilities for producing and transporting oil and of the various political crises that have affected the area differentially in the period.

In 1946 production was largely concentrated in Iran, where the oil industry development dates from the early years of the century.   Iran, however, lost its position as a result of the crisis following the nationalization of the Iranian oil industry in 1951.   The great Abadan refinery all but completely closed down and there was a cessation of exports.   This situation persisted until 1954, when the political crisis was resolved, and since then production has risen steadily with new developments designed to off-set the declining production from the older fields to the north-east of Abadan.   The consortium of companies that now produces oil on behalf of the National

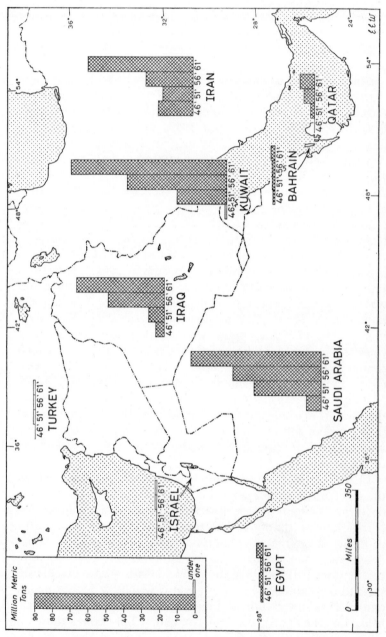

Figure 3. The Changing Pattern of Middle East Oil Production, 1946–61

Iranian Oil Company * has developed the Gach-Saran field, 150 miles east of Abadan. With the construction of a thirty-inch pipeline, with a capacity of over 20 million tons of oil a year, to a new export terminal on Kharg Island, twenty-two miles off the mainland, where tankers of up to 100,000 tons can be loaded, the export potential of the field has been substantially increased. Off-shore exploration in the vicinity of Kharg Island has produced evidence of a new field whose output may also be channelled through the export facilities on the island. Discoveries of oil only eighty miles south of Teheran seem likely to produce sufficient for local consumption and thus eliminate the long and difficult back-haul of products from the Abadan refinery. The Iranian Government's need for increasing oil revenues seems likely to ensure a continuation of the present situation in which increased production is encouraged.

Saudi Arabia was second in importance to Iran in 1946 and is now second to Kuwait. Production has increased steadily over the whole period. New fields have been discovered with great regularity and the productive areas of the established ones constantly extended. The Ghawar field, for example, first discovered in 1948, is now one of the largest in the world. It is already known to be more than 150 miles long and is still being extended. The area of the Safaniya field, brought into production in 1957, was doubled in 1960 and is now the largest off-shore field in the world. Its output increased from 4 million tons in 1959 to over 9 million tons in 1961. Saudi Arabia's proven reserves, thought to be about 7000 million tons, are second only to those of Kuwait and are 50 per cent. greater than the proved reserves of the United States. These vast reserves provide the basis for a continuing rise in output, particularly as the ownership of production has now been diversified with the development of the Neutral Zone off-shore facilities by a Japanese company which started to ship oil in 1961.

The small production in Iraq in 1946 came entirely from the north-east fields from which output has since increased more than ten times. The southern Iraqi fields did not start to produce until 1952 but now provide about 25 per cent. of the

---

* This arrangement was made under the terms of the 1954 agreement. Ownership of the oil and the fixed assets of the industry are vested in the State.

C

total from the country. Production continued to increase during the early part of the period of disagreement between the government and the Iraq Petroleum Company, but failure to resolve the difficulties eventually led to stagnation in the level of output in 1962. This is likely to persist until the government arranges new organizational means of further exploration and development in the unused areas.

Kuwait was of small importance in 1946 with an output of under 5 million tons. This arose from the fact that little development had been possible during the war, when the need to expand output had generally been concentrated on those fields which were already producing significant quantities in 1939. Since 1946, however, the average annual rate of increase in production has been about 12 per cent. The Burgan and Ahmadi-Magwa fields, which have been responsible for most of the oil production to date, continue to be developed but the North Kuwait field, brought into production only in 1957, is already producing about 10 million tons a year. Moreover, exploration in new areas continues, both in the concession areas of the Kuwait Oil Company (jointly owned by B.P. and Gulf Oil) and in the Kuwait/Saudi Arabian Neutral Zone, where American independent companies are the concessionaires. The off-shore area of Kuwait has recently been awarded to Shell which hopes to produce at least 5 million tons from it in 1965 and thereafter to increase production rapidly to 25 million tons per year. By that time Kuwait seems likely to be producing over 150 million tons a year and may then be rivalling Venezuela for the position as the world's third largest producing country.

Of the other nine sheikdoms of the Persian Gulf only two, Bahrain and Qatar, are established producers. The first discovery of oil on the western side of the Persian Gulf was made in Bahrain in 1932 but there have been no further discoveries there since then and production has been stabilized at about 2·5 million tons a year. In contrast, production in Qatar commenced only in 1949 and has since risen to over 8 million tons a year. This is all produced from the Dukham field, now thought to be approaching its maximum output, but an off-shore field has recently been discovered which seems likely to raise Qatar's production to significantly higher levels.

The seven independent sheikdoms collectively known as the Trucial States are all under concession to Petroleum Development (an associated company of the Iraq Petroleum Company) but discoveries so far have been made only in Abu Dhabi. Although this field—the Murban field—seems to have very considerable potential (some reports have, in fact, indicated that Abu Dhabi is likely to become a second Kuwait) and is located only ten miles inland, the growth of production has been delayed as a result of the difficulty in locating an export terminal on the rocky and hitherto uncharted coast. In the meantime, however, Abu Dhabi joined the ranks of the producing countries in 1962 when an off-shore field, jointly developed by B.P. and C.F.P., was brought into production following the completion of a submarine pipeline to the operating centre and tanker terminal on Das Island, about forty miles from the mainland.

Oil production in the rest of the world—Europe, Africa, the Far East and Australasia—amounts to less than 7 per cent. of the global total. The only producing countries of international significance are Indonesia, Algeria and Rumania. Production in Indonesia is about 20 million tons a year (with another 4 million tons from nearby areas in British Borneo). This early oil producing area (production first started in 1890) suffered severe damage during the Second World War, when output was reduced to very small amounts. As a result of immediate post-war rehabilitation, there has been a threefold increase in output since 1950, but in the absence of any major discoveries and in the face of political difficulties between the major producers and the strongly nationalistic Indonesian government, which has not granted any new concessions since 1949, the Indonesian contribution to total world oil production has steadily declined. It is as yet impossible to assess the likely impact of the state controlled development efforts, which are being supported by help from Japan and from Rumania.*

Rumania is the only producer of significance, apart from the Soviet Union itself, in the Sino-Soviet group of countries.

* These efforts will now be supplemented as a result of the agreement in 1962 by several North American oil companies to explore for and to produce oil on behalf of the Indonesian state oil enterprise, Pertamin.

Production from the old established fields, mainly near Ploesti, reached a peak of 8·7 million tons as long ago as 1936.   Partly as a result of wartime damage this fell to less than 4 million tons by 1947, since when there has been some increase.   However, the doubling of Rumanian production from 5 million tons in 1950 to 10·5 million in 1955 was mainly accounted for by the discovery and development of new areas in the south (Oltenia and Pilesti) and the north-east (Moldavia).   The second five-year plan envisaged an increase in production to 13·5 million tons by 1960, but this level was not achieved (1960 production was only 11·4 million tons) and the present plan calls for an increase only to a little over 12 million tons by 1965, indicating that no important new discoveries are anticipated.

In contrast with Indonesia and Rumania, the development of large scale oil production in Algeria is a recent phenomenon. This is in part a reflection of the difficulties of the physical environment in the Sahara, but in larger part it indicates the general lack of interest in the area among the oil companies, whose attention was riveted on the Middle East in spite of North Africa's greater proximity to the Western European markets.   However, French state enterprise persisted in its efforts to secure a supply of oil that would involve France in no foreign exchange expenditure.   This perseverance was re-garded as 'the pursuit of a mirage', but in 1955 the mirage became a reality with the first major discoveries of oil, and thereafter various commercial companies willingly went into partnership with the French for further exploration and development.   As the result of intensive effort, which was stimulated by the oil shortage in Western Europe at the time of the Suez crisis, and with the prospects of Saharan oil securing a privileged position in the French and possibly the European Economic Community markets, production was initiated in 1958.   In 1961 it reached a level of 16 million tons.   Although there may be temporary setbacks to the growth in output as a result of the difficulties accompanying the transfer of political power, the new Algerian government is committed to maintain a favourable atmosphere for the further development of the industry.   This, combined with the advantage of location in relation to the European market, seems likely to result in a larger Algerian contribution to world oil supplies by the mid-1960s.

Elsewhere in the world, petroleum production is only of local significance as, for example, in Germany, where an annual production of about 6 million tons meets about 15 per cent. of domestic demand, and in Austria, where an output of under 2·5 million tons fills about 60 per cent. of market requirements. However, there are three African countries which seem likely in the next few years to make a contribution to the world oil industry. These are Nigeria, Gabon and Libya.

Oil exploration began in Nigeria in 1937 but it had to be suspended during the war and was not resumed until 1947. Another nine years went by before oil was finally discovered in 1956. Since then five fields in the eastern deltaic region of the Niger have been brought into production and the country's total output increased rapidly from 300,000 tons in 1958 to about 2·2 million tons in 1961. Steady expansion of output from these fields is expected during the 1960s as facilities for exporting and refining the oil are developed, and by the end of the decade an annual production of about 10 million tons per annum is expected. However, there are also prospects for oil development to the west of the River Niger, where several American and other non-British companies were granted concession rights early in 1962. If these efforts are successful Nigerian production may be significantly higher than 10 million tons by 1970.

Oil production in former French Equatorial Africa (Gabon and the Congo Republic) started in 1957 and had risen to over 1 million tons by 1961. Production from the existing fields seems unlikely to go ahead very quickly, but new exploration by a French state company, in conjunction with Shell and Mobil, both on-shore and off-shore, could lead to significant increases in the output of the area by the mid-1960s.

Of much greater immediate significance is the prospect of rapidly increasing production from Libya, where the search for oil did not start until 1955, but which quickly became a favoured exploration area as a result of the discoveries at that time of important fields just across the Algerian border and the introduction of a new Libyan oil law, which by its favourable terms encouraged oil companies to seek concessions. By 1960 almost the whole of the country was either under concession or sought by prospective concessionaires, who in their eagerness to secure the more favourable areas offered terms better than the 1955 law demanded.   Oil was first discovered in 1958 and since then no fewer than twenty-five oil producing structures have been located.   The 150 producer wells at the end of 1961 have a potential yield of at least 12 million tons per year. Actual production has had to await the completion of export facilities but the first development was complete by 1961. This was a thirty-inch pipeline over the 110 miles from the Zelten field to the export terminal at Marsa el Brega.   In the last few months of 1961 500,000 tons were exported, but in the first full year of operation, exports increased to over 6 million tons, and it is expected that by 1963 the pipeline will be used to its 8·25 million tons capacity, which, however, can easily be increased by the addition of more pumping stations when the need arises.   Pipelines from two other fields are under construction and should be carrying another 7 million tons of oil a year to the coast by mid-1963.   Thus, less than five years after the first discovery of oil in Libya the country's annual production will probably exceed 15 million tons.   By the end of the 1960s, Libya seems certain to be ranked among the world's major petroleum exporting countries, although the extremely favourable petroleum law of 1955 has now been modified so that it offers much less attractive conditions for exploration and production.   The modified law, however, together with the practice of inviting competitive bids for new and relinquished concessions, only brings Libya into line with other major producing countries.   Libya should, therefore, continue to attract investment with the oil companies anxious to take advantage of the fact that its territory is attractive for exploration and that Libya is in a favourable location in relation to the major European markets.

The changing distribution of world petroleum production over the last thirty years is summarized in Table 2, in which an estimate of the likely pattern for 1970 is also included.

Some indications of the reasons for this changing pattern of world production have been mentioned in passing in the present chapter but the main factors involved will be examined in detail in Chapter 3.

TABLE 2

THE CHANGING DISTRIBUTION
OF WORLD OIL PRODUCTION, 1930–70

	1930	1940	1950	1960	1970 estimated
World Production (millionmetric tons)	206	300	545	1050	1850
Percentage in					
1 *Western Hemisphere*	78	77	73	56	40
of which: United States	63	64	54	36	21
Canada	..	..	1	3	3
Venezuela	10	9	15	13	11
Rest of Western Hemisphere	5	4	3	4	5
2 *Eastern Hemisphere*	7	10	19	28	38
of which: Middle East	3	5	17	24	28
Far East	4	4	2	3	2
Western Europe	..	..	1	1	2
Africa	..	..	..	1	6
3 *Sino-Soviet Bloc*	15	12	8	15	22
of which: U.S.S.R.	7	9	6	13	20

Sources: Oil Industry Trade Journals.   Author's estimates for 1970

REFERENCES

1 See M. G. de Chazeau and A. E. Kahn *Integration and Competition in the Petroleum Industry* (Petroleum Monograph Series, Vol. 3), 1959, Chapter 7 for an analysis of the prorationing system in the United States.

2 A recent analysis of the distribution of Soviet oil production and potential can be found in J. A. Hodgkins, *Soviet Power*, 1961, pp. 100–133.

3 L. M. Fanning. *Foreign Oil and the Free World.* 1954, p. 356.

CHAPTER 3

The Pattern of Production;
the Determining Factors

The actual pattern of production, within the broad framework set by the success of exploration efforts in developing the discovered reserves and by the establishment of producing and transporting facilities for getting the oil out of the ground and away to the markets, is largely determined by a complex set of political and economic factors. Moreover, even the degree of exploration effort from place to place and the willingness or otherwise of companies to finance developments of discoveries is similarly related to political and economic considerations. The significance of these factors is thus of paramount importance in establishing the distribution of oil producing facilities—and the extent to which they are used—and this chapter is concerned with picking out the main elements that go to make up the complex. The inter-relationship of the factors will, however, become apparent and the influence of each one on the others should be constantly borne in mind.

The Choices Available to the Major International Companies

Outside the United States and the Sino-Soviet sphere, eight giant integrated oil companies are responsible for over 80 per cent. of crude production, 71 per cent. of refining capacity, 35 per cent. of tanker ownership and about 70 per cent. of the distribution and marketing of oil products. Five of the companies are American, viz: Standard Oil of New Jersey (known as Esso or Jersey), Gulf Oil, Standard Oil of New York (Socony-Mobil), Standard Oil of California (Socal or Stancal) and Texas Oil (Texaco). The Royal Dutch/Shell Group (Shell) is Anglo-Dutch, British Petroleum is British owned (51 per cent. owned by the government), and Compagnie

Française des Petroles (C.F.P.), is a French company jointly owned by the State and private shareholders. Each of the eight companies has its own separate facilities but they often form partnerships which carry out specific operations.[1] For example, the Iraq Petroleum Company is a consortium of Jersey, Mobil, Shell, B.P. and C.F.P. concerned with producing and refining oil in Iraq. The Kuwait Oil Company is a joint B.P./Gulf Oil company which holds the exploration and producing concession for about half of mainland Kuwait.* In the United Kingdom Shell and B.P. have a joint marketing arrangement which dates back to 1932. Until recently, Jersey and Socony-Mobil operated a joint company, Stanvac, responsible for all refining and marketing operations east of Suez.

Each of the groups has a complex corporate structure. This is, in part, a reflection of the growth of new activities in new areas over an extended period of time; in part, it is due to local nationalist pressure which makes it imperative in many countries that companies be registered locally; and, in part, it is a desire to achieve the minimum tax obligations possible. As a result of these factors, the Shell Group, for example, consists of over 500 companies engaged in one or more aspects of the oil business in almost every country of the non-communist world. (There are also a dozen or more companies with names such as the Shell Company of Lithuania which remain in existence to maintain a claim to compensation for expropriated facilities.)

Because of their international structure, these companies have endeavoured to secure producing facilities in many different countries of the world. Such a diversification of potential sources of oil they feel to be essential to ensure security of supplies in the face of recurring political crises in one or another of their areas of operations. They also find it essential in many cases to secure facilities in countries where the oil potential is being developed and which may prove to have special advantages. Such advantages could be economic in that the new areas may have such favourable conditions that

---

* The company held concession rights over the whole of mainland Kuwait until June 1962. Rights over half the country were then relinquished and these are likely to be offered to other companies.

low costs of production can be achieved; or they may be located near to the main consuming areas, thus giving low transport costs for the crude, whose price, therefore, can be posted locally at a level higher than would be otherwise possible, thus giving a higher gross return to the producing company. Or advantages may arise from qualitative reasons whereby the new crude could sell at a premium rate or be particularly suitable for balancing refinery out-turn with the product demand in a given market. Of greatest significance, however, are probably the political advantages that can arise, for in most countries of the world governments tend to insist that preference be given to locally produced crude even though this may well be higher cost than that from alternative overseas sources of supply. Thus, companies marketing oil locally may be prevented from importing oil from their associated supplying companies abroad and thus only have the choice of either moving into production in the country concerned or of buying their crude or product requirements from another producer which has local supplies available. Generally in the past, though, it appears, not necessarily in the future, they have chosen the former course of action. As a result of these incentives to extend productive capacity Shell, for example, now produces oil in the United States, Canada, Venezuela, Trinidad, Colombia, Argentina, Algeria, Egypt, Iraq, Iran, Indonesia, New Guinea, Borneo, Germany, Holland, Austria and Nigeria, and is also developing productive capacity and/or exploring in Guatemala, Libya, Qatar, Kuwait, Tanganyika, Gabon and New Zealand. Similarly Standard Oil of New Jersey can draw on supplies from fourteen countries and is looking for oil in six more.

In having thus extended their capacity to produce oil from many countries, the eight international companies obviously have a degree of choice in deciding how best to meet their requirements in a situation in which the demand for oil is normally significantly lower than the potential supply.

Three factors which limit this degree of choice should, however, be noted. The first arises from the companies' needs to secure a return on capital invested. Thus, once they are committed to a given area, they will not lightly abandon productive capacity until their investment is largely depreciated.

The second arises from the restraining influence of what is politically possible or expedient in view of the high degree of dependence of many oil producing countries on the oil industry (see Chapter 8). This means that companies are unable to reduce their operations significantly without jeopardizing their relationships with the government.

Thirdly, there are considerations of the type of crude and quality which have to be taken into account. Crude oil is a very varied product and each crude has its own special characteristics. For example, variations in specific gravity * are significant, for these largely determine the relative yields of main products (though not their quality) on distillation—the simplest and cheapest refining process. Hence some crudes will be more appropriate than others for meeting the demand for products in particular markets. Refineries, moreover, are sometimes built to run on a certain type of crude and thus refinery investment may present a factor limiting changes in the pattern of production. Crudes also vary in their degree of contamination by compounds other than hydro-carbons. Sulphur is one important impurity, for it necessitates special cleansing processes in the refinery to remove it from the lighter products. It cannot economically be extracted from fuel oil, however, and as some industries (*e.g.* cement manufacture) demand a sulphur-free fuel oil, crude oils which provide this may well be lifted more quickly than would otherwise have been the case. Other crudes are of special importance as they are the source of high-value products such as lubricating oils or other special products such as bitumen. Here again quality considerations can affect decisions on the rate of development of a field.

Within these three broad limitations the international companies make an effort to use crude oil on which, after production, transport and other ancillary costs, together with tax and royalty obligations to the governments in the producing countries, have been taken into account, the greatest net profit

* Variations in specific gravity are conventionally measured in degrees A.P.I. These vary inversely with specific gravity. Crudes are divided into three groups according to their S.G.: thus, heavy crudes have an A.P.I. value ranging from 10 to 20° (*e.g.* Laguna crude from Venezuela which is rated 11° A.P.I.); medium crudes vary from 20 to 30° A.P.I. (*e.g.* Safaniya crude from Saudi Arabia rated at 27° A.P.I.); and light crudes have an A.P.I. value of over 30° (*e.g.* Hassi Messaoud crude from the Sahara which is rated 40° A.P.I.).

can be achieved.   In general, Middle Eastern oil is the cheapest
to produce—estimates [2] suggest that average lifting costs are
as low as £1 per ton and that they may fall to only 10s. per ton
in the most favourable conditions—and the integrated companies have, therefore, rapidly increased their supplies from
this source.   Thus, in the period 1958–61, whilst demand for
oil in the world rose by about 7 per cent. per annum, Middle
Eastern production, almost all of which is controlled directly
or indirectly by the eight international companies, increased
by 10 per cent. per year.

For example, not only have Gulf Oil and B.P. rapidly
developed production in Kuwait for their own world-wide
requirements but the former has also succeeded in making
large and continuing sales to the Shell Group, which wished to
secure access to cheap Middle Eastern oil to meet its increasing
European and eastern hemisphere commitments.[3]   Since 1958
it would seem that Shell has found it more profitable to
continue to take increasing quantities of Gulf's Kuwait oil than
even to maintain its own production in Venezuela.   From 1959
to 1961 the Shell Group's total world-wide sales increased by
about 14 per cent. from 125 to 142 million tons.   Over this
period its purchases from Gulf increased by 36 per cent. from
20·5 to 28·0 million tons, while its production in Venezuela
declined by 7 per cent. from 40 to 37 million tons.   The
contribution of Shell's Venezuelan production to the Group's
total sales thus declined from 32 per cent. in 1959 to 26 per cent.
in 1961.[4]   Even with the necessary facilities (such as staff, pipelines, terminal capacity, etc.) to handle additional quantities
of oil from Venezuela, the marginal costs involved together
with the obligations to the Venezuelan government on each
additional barrel of oil produced must, over this period, have
exceeded the cost of purchasing oil from an outside supplier in
the Middle East.

Because of the impact of developments such as this, the
companies operating in Venezuela were estimated in 1961 to
have over 1 million barrels per day of shut-in capacity (this is
equal to an annual output of 50 million tons).   It is, however,
conceivable that there would have been an even greater swing
away from Venezuelan output had not the companies considered it expedient to limit the decline in their offtake because

of the possibilities of expropriation of their assets or other curbs
on their activities by a moderate but insecure government of
the 'left' under Senor Betancourt, who has had to resist
pressure from extremist groups which might have been able
to force the government's hand if the country's economic
difficulties had been made any worse by even lower exports of
oil and reduced tax and royalty payments to the government.
However, such possible repercussions did not, for example,
prevent Gulf Oil, with a large Venezuelan subsidiary, from
offering the Uruguayan state refinery supplies from Kuwait
rather than from the traditional Venezuelan supply point.
Gulf secured the contract—because its prices were lower—
against competition from other companies which offered
Venezuelan oil. Similarly, in Brazil some of the international
companies with oil available from both Venezuela and the
Middle East have supplied Petrobas—the state oil concern—
with crude from the latter area.

It is this element of choice which the international companies
enjoy, in deciding where their productive potential shall be
worked to capacity or even extended or, on the other hand,
left partially unused, that has played a significant part in
helping to change the world pattern of production in recent
years. Thus Venezuela's share of total production has
declined. Over the period 1950–57 the annual average
increase in Venezuela's production was about 9 per cent.—its
rate of expansion was then rather higher than that in the
world as a whole. From 1958 to 1961 the annual rate of
increase in production did not exceed 2 per cent. and the
country's share of the total world output has declined from
16·5 to 13·5 per cent. The 1961 report by the World Bank on
the Venezuelan economy indicated that at least a 4 per cent.
per annum increase in petroleum exports is necessary for a
desirable minimum of economic development.[5] The likelihood
of this being achieved, whilst the major international companies
with production facilities in Venezuela have the ability to
secure their increasing requirements for oil from other parts of
the world, would seem to depend largely upon the actions of the
United States government, which looks upon Venezuela as the
key country in the containment of communist advance in
the whole of the Caribbean area. This political concern for

Venezuela suggests that the United States government will either bring pressure to bear on the American oil companies operating there to increase their offtake * or will give a preferential outlet for Venezuelan oil in the United States market, which is controlled by import quotas. In either case some of the present freedom of choice of the international companies will be restricted.

Within the Middle East, many of the 'majors' can also exercise a choice when making decisions concerning production levels from various countries. Following the closure of its facilities in Iran in 1951, the Anglo-Iranian Oil Company (which later became British Petroleum) was able to switch its main production effort to Kuwait, whose output continued to increase very rapidly even after the Iranian problem had been resolved in 1954. Kuwait production which stood at only 17 million tons in 1950 increased to 43 million tons only three years later and by 1961 had risen to over 85 million tons. In contrast, production in Iran only recovered to its 1950 level of 32 million tons in 1957 and even by 1961 stood at less than three-quarters of Kuwait's output. More recently, the five participating companies in the Iraq Petroleum Company were able to pursue their negotiations with General Kassem in the knowledge that in the event of drastic action by the Iraqi government—such as the nationalization of the company —they could increase production from fields which they control in other Middle Eastern countries and hence eliminate their needs for Iraqi oil in their marketing operations. Their ownership of such a large share of total marketing outlets would probably ensure that much Iraqi oil would not be able to find alternative markets.

Thus, by virtue of their ownership and control of a large part of the international industry, the major international oil companies retain a significant, although, for reasons we shall examine later, a diminishing role in establishing the changing pattern of petroleum production. Until a much larger percentage of market outlets are independent of the international companies, it seems unlikely that any important producing country, on failing to persuade the companies to

---

* It seems possible that the rise of 9 per cent. in Venezuelan production in 1962 was due in part to such pressure.

guarantee increasing output, could successfully take over the operations and hope to market more than a very small percentage of the total marketed by the companies themselves. It seems principally to have been his realization that the interests of the Middle Eastern producing countries are associated with those of the international companies that persuaded the Sheik of Kuwait to grant the important off-shore concession in 1961 to the Shell Group which, although offering less attractive profit sharing possibilities than some of the other companies which applied for the concession, did provide a ready-made world-wide marketing network with more or less guaranteed outlets in other subsidiaries of the Group for the potential production. From Shell's point of view the good prospects of large-scale production from off-shore Kuwait,* with a cost structure probably not dissimilar from that in the on-shore areas, where costs of production are probably lower than anywhere else in the non-communist world, gives the Group even greater flexibility in its choice of sources of supply. Should the demand for its oil grow at a somewhat smaller rate than the company anticipated when seeking the concession, then the production from off-shore Kuwait must adversely affect the expansion of production in the other countries in which the Group has producing interests.

The Impact of the 'Independents'

Until the mid-1950s the major international companies controlled an even greater share of world production and marketing of petroleum than they did in 1961 (see page 28). The decline in their share is due in large part to the activities of the so-called 'Independents' of the world petroleum industry. These are mainly United States companies which until the last few years produced, refined and marketed oil only in North America. However, in the 1950s they were persuaded to move out into the rest of the world by the feeling at that time that the indigenous supplies of oil in the United States would soon become insufficient to meet the then rapidly growing demand. Moreover, it was also becoming more and more apparent that the difference in the price of oil at home

* There was a show of oil with the first well drilled in July 1962—only a few months after exploration work started.

and abroad was widening to such an extent that foreign oil would soon be able to undercut domestically produced oil even in interior areas of the United States. Influenced by these considerations, and also by the favourable tax treatment which they could obtain in their overseas operations, the leading United States independent companies sought and obtained concessions in several parts of the world. Aminoil, a consortium of nine of the leading United States domestic companies, and Getty Oil had secured concessions in the Saudi Arabian/Kuwait neutral zone as early as 1950, and these were joined in the Middle East by other companies a few years later (*e.g.* Pan American Petroleum in Iran in 1958). The decision by Pérez Jiménez to auction concessions in Venezuela provided important opportunities for the 'Independents'. United States domestic companies (for example, Continental Oil, which now owns Jet Petroleum Company) also moved into Libya after the 1955 petroleum law made exploration efforts there more attractive. The concessions purchased were, in many cases, extremely favourable for quick exploitation (for example, those of the Lake Maracaibo region of Venezuela) and the companies concerned went rapidly ahead in an attempt to secure oil production as quickly as possible. Thus, Superior Oil brought their concessionary areas in Venezuela into production in 1959, the Pan American Petroleum Corporation discovered oil in its Iranian off-shore area in 1961, and Ohio Oil and its two associated companies, Continental Oil and Amerada, commenced exports from one of the Group's Libyan concessions in the spring of 1962.

In 1961 the contribution of the American 'Independents' to total production in Venezuela was 27 million tons—18 per cent. of the country's total (compared with only 8 per cent. of a much smaller level of production in 1955). From the Kuwait/Saudi Arabian Neutral Zone the two American Companies that operate the concession jointly achieved a record output of 9 million tons. Thus, these independent American companies, as a result of their operations in various parts of the world, have raised production, and, to an even greater degree, productive capacity to levels higher than the international companies probably anticipated when they were making their plans for this period. It might thus be supposed that the individual countries in which such production has been centred have benefited from this development.

This interpretation can, however, be challenged, at least as far as Venezuela is concerned. The increasing world supply and world potential supply of oil, in part the result of the new foreign operations by the foregoing United States Companies, has intensified competition for world markets with resultant falling prices and reduced profit margins. The impact on Venezuela has been two-fold. Royalties and other payments by the companies to the government there are dependent on the prices actually realized for the oil,* and as these have fallen away the government's income per barrel of oil has also declined. In an effort to prevent the erosion of its oil income, the Venezuelan government has sought to prevent sales of oil abroad at prices discounted more than 10 per cent. off the posted price. This has helped to make Venezuelan oil even less competitive with oil from other sources and partly because of this, and partly because of their need to concentrate production on the cheapest sources of supply, the international companies have tended to rationalize their production programmes to the detriment of their Venezuelan operations. The reduction in the level of the Shell Group's production in Venezuela compared with rising sales for the Group in the period since 1958 has already been indicated.

The action of the United States in imposing a system of quotas designed to limit its import of crude oil and products has accentuated the impact of the United States independents on the world oil market. This move, instituted in 1959, was designed to bolster the domestic industry and was made more respectable by reference to strategic reasons. However, no matter what the motive for the action, it had the effect of eliminating the original reasoning that lay behind the decisions of the United States companies to seek supplies outside the United States. These companies intended to produce oil for sale in the United States, but with this market now denied to them outlets had to be sought elsewhere. The West European market provided the only possibility—or at least those countries in West Europe where the refining and marketing of oil is not

---

* This may be contrasted with the position in the Middle East where payments are calculated on the basis of the posted prices.

D

mainly in the hands of the major companies (as it is in the United Kingdom)—and since 1959 a buyers' market has developed in which discounts of up to 40 per cent. off the posted prices have been available.   Though such price weakness may well have increased the demand for oil,* the incremental demand has not been sufficient to compensate for the loss of the anticipated United States outlet and surplus productive capacity remains.

In addition to the United States' independent companies which have initiated oil production from other parts of the world in the period since 1958, companies from other countries have also increased in importance.   Of greatest significance has been Ente Nazionale Idrocarburi (E.N.I.), the Italian state-owned company with interests not only in oil and natural gas but in many other industrial enterprises.   E.N.I.'s incentive to seek oil abroad has arisen from the rapidly growing demand for oil in energy-short Italy and the unwillingness to see the import trade entirely in the hands of foreign enterprise.   The same explanations can perhaps be advanced to explain why Japanese companies have also been formed to explore for and to develop oil producing facilities overseas.   These Italian and Japanese companies have generally been successful in obtaining concessions in areas with a high potential by their willingness to offer more favourable terms than the international companies to the governments of the host countries.   They have not, for example, been bound by the traditional '50 : 50' arrangement in the Middle East whereby profits are shared equally by the producing company and the producing country. Thus, the Japan–Arabian Oil company secured concessions in the off-shore Neutral Zone of Saudi Arabia and Kuwait in 1958.   By mid-1962, only two years after the first discovery of oil, the company had already achieved a production capacity of 200,000 barrels per day (equal to 10 million tons per year). E.N.I. was willing to enter into partnership (a form of operation unwelcome to the international companies as it restricts their freedom of action, but very welcome indeed to a producing country with an infant state-owned oil company which needs advice and technical assistance and probably financial help)

---

* Most probably as a result of an increased rate of substitution of coal by oil— see below p. 86 *et seq.*

with the National Iranian Oil Company. This arrangement dates from September 1957 and production of the order of 1·5 million tons is expected in 1963. E.N.I. and other European companies from France, Germany and Sweden have more recently secured concessions in Libya and should be contributing to the growing production from this area within a relatively short time. Thus, the impact of these non-American independent companies—whose influence seems likely to grow as European and Japanese demand for oil expands very quickly—has been to reinforce the effect of the United States independents by bringing new areas into production and increasing production from other areas rather more quickly than would have been likely had the international companies not had to face this new competition.

The Influence of Political and Economic Nationalism

The two factors so far discussed are essentially ones which have tended to concentrate petroleum production in the world's most prolific areas—viz: Venezuela, and more especially, the Middle East and its extension into North Africa. Such an areally limited pattern of world oil production is, however, unacceptable to a large group of countries which for various nationalistic reasons do not wish to import their supplies of oil. We have, for example, already shown that even the United States for reasons of economic nationalism—the protection of the domestic industry and an autarkic resources policy—has discouraged oil imports from overseas by a system of quotas which have the effect of limiting imports to the amounts needed to fill the gap between domestic output and requirements. Policies of various kinds, but with much the same overall effect, have been adopted by many other countries, especially those which are largely dependent upon oil for energy supplies and therefore view it as a strategic resource, and those which can ill-afford large import bills for oil as a result of their inability to export sufficient goods to pay for their imports. The latter consideration applies to most of the nations which are numbered among the developing countries, for they generally produce foodstuffs and raw materials, the demand for which is not growing very rapidly among the industrial nations, and they also have a rapidly increasing demand for energy as a result of the changing structure of their economies with its greater emphasis on industrialization.

As far as the world pattern of oil production is concerned, the effect of such attitudes is a tendency to diversify the sources of production as the countries concerned aim to achieve and to maximize indigenous production of oil largely irrespective of any consideration of comparative costs. Such diversification, is, however, sometimes modified by the further expression of nationalism whereby certain countries will only permit exploitation of their oil resources by national (generally state) enterprise. Hence, because of the all too frequent shortage of the large amounts of capital necessary for a really intensive exploration and development effort, oil production does not go ahead as rapidly as it might were foreign risk capital acceptable for the enterprise.

The effect of these considerations is seen in Argentina and Brazil. These two countries are among the world's major consumers of petroleum, which provides over 80 per cent. of total commercial energy demand in Argentina and more than 70 per cent. in Brazil. Under the impact of structural change in their economies with particular emphasis on industrialization, energy use has been increasing rapidly—at an average annual rate of almost 10 per cent. in Brazil since 1950 and at about 5·5 per cent. per annum over the same period in Argentina. This process is continuing with further advance towards industrialization and both countries have had to face the problem of minimizing expenditure on petroleum imports which, by 1958, were accounting for over 20 per cent. of their total import bills.

Petroleum production in both countries has been exclusively reserved to state enterprise—to Yacimientos Petrolíferos Fiscales (Y.P.F.) in Argentina (though Shell and Jersey were allowed to continue production on a small scale from the fields they had developed prior to the formation of Y.P.F. in 1935) and to Petrobras in Brazil. In Argentina, Y.P.F. gradually managed to lift production from 3 million tons in 1948 to about 5 million tons ten years later. Although this increase in oil production of over 60 per cent. in ten years was viewed and presented as a success story by Argentina's politicians, domestic production was by the late 1950s only providing about one-third of the country's total requirements with a consequent deleterious effect on the balance of trade caused by the need to import the balance of oil products required.

Yet these difficulties over the foreign exchange cost of oil were unnecessary, for reserves of both petroleum and natural gas had been proven in several parts of the country and possible reserves existed in more extensive areas. The factor that inhibited development at a rate sufficiently rapid to close the gap between domestic production and total demand was the insistence, for nationalistic reasons, that the industry be reserved to the state company and the inability of that enterprise to secure enough capital for the development of producing and transport facilities. Rigid price control over petroleum products prevented self-financing by the Y.P.F. and the government generally had other calls on its available finance which were given priority over the requirements of the oil industry.

In the latter part of his period of government even Perón, Argentina's dictator since 1944, recognized the need for a change of policy and opened negotiations with an American oil company for the possible development of the proved reserves. These negotiations were, however, used by Perón's opponents to rouse popular feeling against him and with his overthrow in 1956 they were dropped. President Frondizi elected in 1958 had, in his election campaign, promised to maintain the nationalist attitude and policies whereby petroleum development was reserved to Y.P.F. Following his election, however, Frondizi recognized the illogicality of a situation whereby the country's petroleum resources remained in the ground while, at the same time, scarce foreign exchange was used to finance the import of the bulk of the nation's oil requirements. In the face of strong opposition, exploration and production contracts were speedily signed with various international and United States oil companies which quickly moved in to develop the proven areas and to explore in other parts of the country. The willingness of the international companies marketing oil in Argentina, who had been accustomed to importing their requirements of crude and products, to accept commitments for additional capital expenditure on production in a country where the costs were likely to exceed greatly those in the major producing areas of the world, arose from the appreciation that once domestic oil became available the facilities for importing their own requirements would be withdrawn. Their only alternative would have been to purchase oil from those companies which did secure local production and this was even less acceptable.

Thus, with economic nationalism achieving a more dominant role than political nationalism, Argentina has rapidly achieved self-sufficiency in oil and production rose from 5 million tons in 1958 to over 12·5 million tons in 1961. With local production given absolute protection against competition from overseas supplies, it seems likely that domestic production can match the rising demand for most of the rest of the decade, particularly if plans to utilize the natural gas reserves associated with the oil fields are fulfilled.

In Brazil, in spite of several recent changes of government, political nationalism has maintained its influence and the political slogan 'petroleo e nosso' (petroleum is ours) still has an over-riding effect. This perhaps arises in part from the relative success of Petrobras in increasing oil production. When Petrobras was formed there was no oil production to speak of in Brazil and the international companies had shown no interest in exploration efforts, perhaps owing to the proximity of their large scale production in Venezuela. By 1961 Petrobras had achieved a level of production of about 4·5 million tons—sufficient to meet almost one-third of total demand. In the late 1950s it is likely that a relaxation of the nationalistic attitude would have persuaded foreign companies to join in the search for oil as in Argentina with the object of lifting production to levels more in line with local demand. However, a recent report [6] on the possibilities of petroleum development in Brazil has given a very unfavourable picture, with prospects rated poor for the discovery of oil in commercial quantities other than in Eastern Bahia, where present production is located. In the light of this report it now seems much less certain that a retreat from political to economic nationalism, whereby domestic production is given precedence over imports, would attract foreign risk capital for exploration. In taking a decision the international companies would certainly take cognizance of the unfavourable conditions for marketing oil in Brazil owing to government intervention and control at all stages of the operation. Gulf Oil has already withdrawn from the country and Shell and Jersey are probably persuaded not to do likewise only by their unwillingness to abandon considerable capital assets and by the hope that in the longer-term future their patience may be rewarded by a profitable and expanding market in what seems likely to be one of the most important countries of the late twentieth century. Thus Petrobras will probably continue to 'go it alone' with a redoubling of its efforts to produce in Brazil a larger percentage of the country's total demand and perhaps aided by financial and technical assistance from either or both of the United States and the Soviet Union.

Economic nationalism was largely responsible for the initial development of oil exploration and production in North Africa. In spite of knowledge of the broad sedimentary belt lying across the whole of the region and its proximity to the important West European market, little interest was shown in the area by the international companies, which preferred the greater certainties of the Middle East for their main exploration efforts. The incentive to probe the area for its resources arose from France's post-war balance of payments and other reconstruction problems, which necessitated the development of the French Union in order to minimize foreign exchange commitments for oil. The newly formed state entity, Bureau de Recherches de Petrole, initiated exploration in Morocco, Algeria and Tunisia. It was not until 1955 that French national enterprise and faith was rewarded with the discovery of the major field at Edjele. Thereafter, major finds were made in rapid succession and many companies moved in to stake their claims not only in Algeria but also in Morocco and Tunisia, which were by then independent, and in adjoining areas of Libya and Spanish Morocco. In part, interest in these other countries arose from the great promise of the area, in part from the prospect of reducing dependence on Middle Eastern supplies, of which by the late 1950s, some ten years and several crises later, the international companies were rather less sure, and in part from the favourable location of the area in relation to the rapidly expanding European market.

However, the underlying motivation to exploration and development in Algeria and the Sahara has been the knowledge that France cherished the long-term ambition of self-sufficiency in oil and intended, therefore, to give preference to supplies from this source.   The pattern of crude supply to the French refineries would not depend primarily on the judgement of the operating companies but first and foremost on how great a percentage of the demand could be met with French oil. The French market is not only expanding rapidly (consumption increased from 14 million tons in 1954 to over 21 million tons in 1961) but is also highly profitable because of the limitation of competition by the government, which has a large stake in the industry.   The international companies marketing there were thus so anxious to secure their own Algerian supplies that they set aside their dislike of joint ventures with national capital and willingly entered into partnership with French concerns, as they were obliged to do before being permitted by the French government to exploit French territory for its oil resources.   The French government maintains its intention that French refineries shall use as much franc oil as possible (for 1962 the aim was 35 per cent.) and, moreover, an extension of this nationalistic approach is being attempted as France endeavours to secure unlimited openings for Saharan oil in the whole of the European Common Market and also attempts to restrict its imports from the rest of the world.   In this respect, France has so far won a partial victory by having the Common Market agree that, in the event of a common external tariff being imposed on petroleum products, then those from the Netherlands Antilles (where they are refined from Venezuelan crude) shall only have preferential entry up to a quota limit.

Nationalist desires for increased domestic output of oil have sometimes—as in Argentina until 1958—been held in check by the unwillingness or inability of the country concerned to attract and retain overseas companies willing to explore for oil. This has perhaps been the main reason behind the long-delayed discovery of oil in commercial quantities in Australia, where it was only in 1961 that the first commercial field was located in spite of about thirty years of intermittent efforts.   In lieu of success in attracting international capital and expertise for the job, there have often been national efforts to achieve the

desired result but these have sometimes also failed because of
the lack of funds and technical know-how. Contrasting with
their heavy exploration expenditure in the earlier part of the
decade, the international companies have not, since the late
1950s when it became apparent that they were entering on a
lengthy period when the potential supply of oil was to exceed
the demand, been particularly keen to search for oil here,
there and everywhere unless there were especially compelling
reasons why they should. They have sufficient sources of
supply to keep pace with their increasing requirements from
their growing potential of production in the main centres of
development, where costs are at their lowest and profits at their
highest.

The impact of this and the reaction to it is seen in India and
Pakistan, which have balance of payments problems similar
to those of Argentina and Brazil and wish to expand the
indigenous production of energy in order to save foreign
exchange on importing oil. Searches by the major companies
in these two countries have met with little success. The
reasons advanced for this have varied from party to party;
the companies suggest that it is due to physical causes and the
failure of the governments to create sufficiently favourable
economic climates to encourage their work. Nationalist
feeling retorts that the companies have been insufficiently
diligent and have not explored as intensively as they might
because of their preference to continue supplying the area with
cheap-to-produce Middle East crude and products. However,
no matter what the main reason, national needs and feelings
have not been assuaged and in both countries state enterprises
have been started to pursue the search for oil.

Technical and financial limitations have, until recently,
been an important restraining influence on developments but a
situation is now developing whereby these limitations may, in
part at least, be overcome. This arises from the willingness of
the Soviet Union to advance credits and technical assistance
for oil industry projects in the developing countries. An
examination of the motivations for this aid lies beyond the
scope of this book [7] but its impact on the world pattern of oil
production could become of significance as the ability of the
Soviet Union to extend aid to strengthen national oil industries

is gradually increased. This it will be in a position to do as a result of the rapid expansion of its own domestic industry, from which surplus equipment and technicians can be deployed overseas and to which overseas trainees can be invited to be not only trained in technical matters but also advised on the advantages to be derived from the development of the industry by the state rather than by private enterprise.

Soviet aid already committed for oil industry development in the non-communist world amounts to about £170 million, of which some 36 per cent. has either been spent or promised to the Indian state oil enterprise. Soviet financed exploration under the Indian second five-year plan has led to the development of the Cambay field. Further development of the field and the construction of facilities to transport and refine the oil will be financed by the Soviet Union during India's current third five-year plan. In Pakistan, after evaluating the prospects for oil development, the Soviet Union has offered a loan of over £11 million for exploration purposes. This has been accepted by Pakistan—the first occasion it has accepted help from the communist world—and the search is under way. As the search is taking place in areas from which western companies have previously withdrawn on the grounds that no oil in commercial quantities was likely to be found, success in this venture, as well as opening up an entirely new area of oil production, could also be politically embarassing. Elsewhere in the world, Soviet help is being given for exploration and development purposes in Syria, Egypt, Afghanistan and Cuba. Rumania has also offered to help national developments in Brazil and Indonesia. The impact of Soviet help will obviously contribute to the extension and further diversification of the world's producing areas.

A similar effect is also being achieved by the activities of another state enterprise—the Italian E.N.I., whose projects in the major producing areas have already been examined (see page 38). E.N.I. also seems to be prepared as a matter of policy, and as part of its 'battle' with the 'seven sisters' (the description given to the major international oil companies by Signor Mattei, the head of E.N.I. until his death in October, 1962), to give financial and other encouragement to state oil developments in other parts of the world. Agreements to assist in producing operations in Argentina and India have been concluded and offers to Mexico and Madagascar have also been reported.

However, neither the Soviet Union nor E.N.I. has openly entered the struggle between the Iraqi government and the Iraq Petroleum Company and its associates, Basrah Petroleum and Mosul Petroleum. Iraq, one of the world's major producing countries (seventh in importance in 1961), conceded the whole of its territory to this single group of foreign companies for the development of its oil resources. The nationalistic policy of General Kassem aimed to curb the powers of the concessionaires and, after the breakdown of long negotiations, the Iraqi government announced in 1962 that all the unutilized concessions, covering over 99 per cent. of the country's area, were to be given up forthwith. As Iraq depends on its expanding oil industry in order to achieve a steadily rising income which will make general economic development possible, it seems possible that the Soviet Union and E.N.I. will make offers of assistance whereby the areas previously conceded to the I.P.C. can be developed. However, the ability of the Soviet Union, and of E.N.I. except in a relatively limited degree, to help find markets for the oil of a major exporting nation has not yet been demonstrated. It will necessitate methods of assistance different from those which are suitable for satisfying the nationalistic aims pursued by many countries in their energy policies. Russia would find its most difficult task not in physically maintaining or even increasing production of Iraqi oil but rather in finding markets for it. In effect, the Soviet Union would have to act as broker for the commodity. But, as the next section of this chapter will show, present indications are that Russia needs and plans to export its own surplus oil in increasing quantities and would be unwilling to replace it with oil from Iraq, which would bring in no return in foreign exchange. Neither is there any real indication that the Soviet Union will be able to place large quantities of oil additional to its own on the world market where facilities for handling, storing and distributing products remain largely in the hands of the major international companies, which would of course be unwilling to help. Because of these limiting factors it is likely to be many years before the economic strength of the Soviet Union could be employed to develop the productive capacity of the world's major exporting regions and countries.

Increasing Production in the Soviet Bloc

Table 2 (page 27) showed that in the period 1950–60, oil production in the Soviet bloc rose from 8 to 15 per cent. of the world total. Of the bloc's total production about 90 per cent. comes from the Soviet Union itself, which is pushing ahead very rapidly with the development of its oil industry. During the Second World War much productive capacity was destroyed, and output in 1945 was only 19·5 million tons. By 1950 this had increased slowly to 37·9 million tons and in the next five years there was a rather more significant rise to 70·7 million tons. In 1955 there began a period of rapid expansion with large annual increases in production. By 1958 output was 113 million tons and in the following three years the annual increases in production were 16, 18 and 19 million tons, so that an output of 166 million tons was achieved in 1961. By 1965, under the terms of the seven-year plan due to end in that year, output was to increase to 230–240 million tons, but this target now seems certain to be exceeded and production should in fact top 250 million tons. At the 22nd Communist Party Congress in October 1961 Kruschchev announced that the Soviet Union would produce 390 million tons of oil in 1970 bringing output within reach of that of the United States. The rapidly increasing production and the great potential that is envisaged is in part a reflection of the favourable physical conditions for oil production in the vast areas of the Soviet Union, which contains more than half as much again potentially petroliferous areas as the United States. The increase in production has come largely from newly discovered and developed areas. Output from the old established North Caucasus, Baku and Sakhalin fields is little larger now than it was in 1938, but whereas these fields then accounted for about three-quarters of the Soviet Union's total production they now provide only 20 per cent. of the total. The most significant development to date has been the growth of output from the fields of the Volga-Urals area. First production from the Volga-Urals was not achieved until 1938 and it was not until after the war that full advantage could be taken of the potential of the area. It now accounts for over two-thirds of the country's total production and major discoveries are still being made. The area from which production is being obtained is of the same size as the producing areas of the Middle East and production in 1961 was about 40 per cent. as great. This gap in production is likely to diminish in the next few years, for while output from the Volga-Urals is expected to double by 1965 that from the Middle East will probably increase by only about 50 per cent., even in the absence of any political crises. The Volga-Urals area has become known as the 'Second Baku' but increasing attention is now being paid to a potential 'Third Baku' in the Soviet Central Asian republics. There have recently been significant discoveries in Turkmenistan, Uzbekistan and Kazakhstan and it seems certain that important developments will take place though perhaps slowly and with difficulty in the face of adverse topographical conditions. At a later stage there are also prospects from the large new oil area in Siberia to which reference has already been made (see page 8).

The physical advantages for the development of oil production have, however, been backed up by the politico-economic needs of the Soviet Union for a rapidly expanding oil industry and made possible by the organization and technology of the Soviet system. In large part the attitude of the Soviet Union to its oil industry is the ultimate expression of the impact of economic nationalism such as was examined in the cases of other countries in the previous section. The divorce between the economic and financial system of the communist world and that of the capitalist world has meant that decisions concerning production within the U.S.S.R. have been totally unrelated to any consideration of relative costs and the theory of comparative advantage. Thus, for the Soviet Union the question of foreign competition does not arise if, as in the case of oil, the domestic resource is able to satisfy planned needs.* Within this

* This situation might be contrasted with that in the United States, where domestic production of oil could be greatly increased if the only consideration were the maximization of production. Producers in the United States, however, are more concerned with price levels than with production levels and also have to take into account other factors such as the availability of cheaper overseas supplies of oil even though these have recently been restricted to some extent by import controls.

deliberate autarkic energy policy, rationalization of the production of different forms of energy is the aim of Soviet planners. The task of working out an optimum structure for energy production has been described by Soviet writers as 'the provision in the most economical way for the growing needs of the economy for fuel and electricity, with due consideration for proper and reliable fuel and power supply'.[8] It is further described as a complex task with account having to be taken of production, distribution and storage costs, the future availability of different fuels, the use of obligatory power resources (e.g. the supply of residual fuel oil produced at a given consumption of lighter fractions), air pollution, changes in labour productivity, etc.[4] As a result of their deliberations the Soviet planners have concluded that proven energy reserves ensure the availability to meet rapidly increasing needs 'for a very long time' and that cheaper supplies of fuel will be made available by limiting the rate of growth or even reducing the output of deep-mined coal and expanding the development of large and economical deposits of oil, natural gas and open-cast coal.[9]

The effect of implementing these plans during the period 1958–70, when the total production of energy is to increase from 685 to almost 1500 million metric tons of coal equivalent in order to provide for the needs of an economy expanding at an annual rate of about 7 per cent., will be to place a greater responsibility on the oil industry in meeting the nation's needs. Whereas the percentage of coal in the total supply of energy will fall from 57 per cent. in 1959 to 42 per cent. in 1965 and to under 35 per cent. by 1970, the contribution of oil will increase from 28 per cent. at the earlier date, to 33 per cent. by 1965 and to almost 40 per cent. by 1972. Thus, the Soviet Union is in the middle of the process of changing from a coal to an oil (and natural gas) based economy and it is this fact which is of most significance in explaining the rising share of the world's petroleum output originating from the Soviet Union. By 1970 oil production in the Soviet Union seems likely to account for well over a fifth of the world's total.

Two other considerations have motivated the Soviet Union to apply sufficient manpower and capital to the oil industry to secure a rapid increase in production. With the exception of Rumania and Albania, the other communist countries are not self-sufficient in oil supplies and their plans for economic development have, therefore, had to make provision for the imports necessary to meet the balance of demand. Within the communist world the key position of energy in the development of national economies is fully recognized and the supply of oil is one of the principal matters on which there has been effective co-operation under the auspices of the Council for Mutual Economic Assistance (COMECON)—the Soviet bloc's equivalent of the Organization for European Economic Co-operation and its successor, the Organization for European Co-operation and Development. An agreement for the continued supply of almost all Eastern Europe's growing requirements for oil by the Soviet Union has been drawn up and detailed plans for the period up to 1965 have been made. Except for certain specialized products and for occasional 'spot' cargoes required to meet unforeseen imbalances, it seems unlikely that western oil companies will have any opportunities of competing for business in Eastern Europe which may, therefore, be viewed as an extension of the Soviet Union's domestic market and thus place on the oil industry of the U.S.S.R. obligations which have to be met. As economic integration in the Soviet bloc seems likely to be more rather than less effective in the next decade, these obligations have no doubt had to be taken into account when the plans for the expansion of the Soviet oil industry were drawn up. The Soviet Union's oil exports in 1961 to the rest of the communist bloc—of the order of 15 million tons—seem likely to be more than doubled by 1970, when they will account for about 8 per cent. of total Soviet production. The level of exports may, however, be much higher if the Soviet Union has to continue to make up deficiencies in Chinese supply. The Soviet Union's relationship with China on oil matters is certainly not as close as that between the Soviet Union and Eastern Europe, and there is some evidence that the U.S.S.R. has been attempting to minimize its commitments partly because of the long and expensive supply routes involved. Moreover, exports via the Trans-Siberian railway are using a route which is working to capacity in transporting material for the economic development of the Soviet Far East—a regional project which seems to have high priority in Soviet planning.   However, in view of China's difficulties in buying oil from United States companies or from non-American companies which do large scale business in the United States or with United States oil purchasing agencies (for military or for economic aid purposes) and hence fear retaliation if they trade with China,* the Soviet Union seems likely to plan its production with at least the intention of meeting China's minimum requirements.   Chinese production is planned to increase rapidly—it has reportedly risen from under 1 million tons in 1955 to over 5 million tons in 1960—for there are great areas of the country which are potentially petroliferous (see Figure 1).   The problem of Soviet supplies to China may thus be only a short-term one and in any case will be eased considerably when the crude pipeline from the Volga-Urals fields is complete through to the Pacific some 4000 miles away.

The other consideration influencing production targets has been the decision of the Soviet Union to re-establish itself as a large-scale exporting nation to countries outside the Soviet bloc. Russia was a significant exporting country up to the First World War but after the upheaval occasioned by the revolution it was several years before the Soviet oil industry was producing a surplus available for export.   By the mid-1930s, however, about 15 per cent. of total Soviet production was being exported. Exports fell away towards the outbreak of war as the expanding economy of the country absorbed increasing amounts, and thereafter Soviet supplies were virtually eliminated from world markets until 1955, except for special arrangements with countries such as Finland and for limited sales to other parts of Western Europe.   Since 1955, however, exports to the non-communist world have increased from less than 4 million tons, representing only 0·5 per cent. of total world supplies, to about 27 million tons in 1961 when they accounted for about 3·0 per cent. of total supplies in the non-communist world.

---

* Sales by Shell to Communist China were extensively reported and adversely commented on in the American press in the early months of 1961. The sales ceased soon after this publicity.

It seems probable that until 1957 the Soviet Union merely used an unplanned and uncertain availability of petroleum products (plus smaller amounts of crude oil) to take advantage of what market opportunities there were in Western Europe at a time when in general there was no overall surplus of oil in the supply area. In 1958, however, the Soviet Union probably began to plan its oil exports and probably wrote these requirements for oil for the non-communist world into its overall development plan for the oil industry. Present indications suggest that the Soviet oil industry is scheduled to provide at least 35 million tons of oil for non-communist markets by 1965 and that thereafter these exports will expand at about the same rate as Soviet production in general—about 10 per cent. per annum until 1970.

This development in Soviet oil policy arises from a growing Soviet appreciation of the significance of oil in the furtherance of its economic and political aims. The rapid industrialization of the Soviet Union demands large and increasing imports of machinery and other capital goods from Western Europe and Japan, and in return the only commodity that is acceptable in large quantities, providing the price is competitive, and with few fears over difficulties in quality, is oil. Hence Soviet oil exports to Western Europe, which since 1957 has taken about 75 per cent. of the total oil exported, appear to have been essentially motivated by sound economic arguments and, on balance, have probably had a favourable economic impact in Europe, where they have introduced an additional competitive factor into the oil market with resultant lower prices for consumers and where they have also provided a reasonably sound basis for the longer-term expansion of East-West trade. The Soviet Union would apparently wish to expand this mutually advantageous exchange with Western Europe so that it would eventually supply about 15 per cent. of Western Europe's oil needs compared with the 1961 level of about 10 per cent. Whether it will be able to do so depends on the moves that are being made to restrict such Russian exports on ideological and strategic grounds under pressure from the United States and other western governments, which in turn are influenced by some of the major international oil companies, which argue that they are unable to compete with oil on which

E

no royalties have been paid * and which is backed by the political and economic resources of the Soviet state. The companies tend to blame this Soviet oil for being the main cause of the low realized prices and profits in Western Europe.

If restrictions on Soviet oil exports to Western Europe are imposed, the political aspect of Soviet oil export policy seems certain to be accentuated as the Soviet Union is forced to seek outlets in the rest of the world—essentially in the developing countries—for the planned quantities of oil that are to be produced for the export programme. Soviet exports to the developing countries—though sometimes in exchange for commodities which the Societ Union has to import—are also very suitable for politically motivated trading relation. Exports to these countries in 1961 totalled about 7 million tons and by 1965 it is probably planned to increase them to about 12 million tons. However, this figure could be almost doubled if Russian oil is diverted from Europe as a result of import restrictions by Western European governments. There seems little doubt that the Soviet Union could win a market for about 24 million tons of oil in these countries by 1965, for it can offer advantages which the western oil companies are not able to match. These include Soviet willingness to exchange the oil either for local goods, which perhaps cannot find an outlet on the world market, or for local non-convertible currency. In both cases the pressure caused by oil imports on the balance of payments is relieved and 'western' oil is replaced.

Moreover, the Soviet Union is usually prepared and is probably always able to sell at prices lower than those charged by the traditional suppliers. In 1960–61, for example, Cuba was reported to have paid, on average, about £5·5 per ton for Soviet oil whereas it had previously paid over £7 per ton for oil imported from nearby Venezuela.† The Soviet contract with India for the supply of kerosene and middle distillates was

---

* It is estimated that, in 1961, E.N.I. contracted to buy Soviet oil at $1.15 per barrel. The companies argue that as their royalties and other payments to governments in the producing countries of the Middle East amount to at least 80 cents per barrel they have no scope whatsoever for competing with the Soviet price.

† The advantageous effect of this cheaper oil on the Cuban balance of payments was, however, later offset by the price of 4 cents per lb. which the Soviet Union paid to Cuba for sugar which had previously been exported to the United States at a premium price of about 5 cents per lb.

reported to allow discounts of 15–18 per cent. off the prices charged by the international companies for their supplies of Middle Eastern oil. It seems that the Soviet Union is in a position to sell its cheapest oil (from the Volga-Urals fields) on what it considers to be a profitable basis at about £3 per ton f.o.b. at a Black Sea port. Italy secured a four year supply of Russian oil at this price in 1961. In the light of royalties and other payments, amounting to at least £2 per ton even in the lowest cost fields, which western companies have to make to the governments of the countries in which they are operating, it seems unlikely that they could get their prices down to the Soviet level. However, even if they could, the Soviet Union could sell even more cheaply to selected countries and view the transaction as aid rather than as trade. In fact, the cost to the Soviet economy of giving away 10 million tons of oil a year would only be about £25 million—an insignificant amount even in relation to the £1000 million aid programme which it has already set up for the developing countries.[10]

Thus, in one market or another, the Soviet Union's plans for re-establishing itself as a large-scale oil exporting nation seem likely to be realized. In that exports planned to go both to the rest of the Communist world and to non-communist areas may, by 1970, account for as much as 25 per cent. of total Soviet oil production, their significance in accounting for the expansion of the Soviet oil industry at a rate faster than that in the rest of the world should not be overlooked.

REFERENCES

1 See W. A. Leeman *The Price of Middle Eastern Oil*, 1962, pp. 15–37 and 153–169 for an analysis of the motives for some of these partnerships.

2 International Bank for Reconstruction and Development, *The Economic Development of Venezuela*, 1961, p. 128.

3 W. A. Leeman, *op. cit.* gives details of the contract, pp. 161–165.

4 Annual Reports of the Royal Dutch/Shell Group and of the Gulf Oil Corporation for 1959 and 1961. Also *Petroleum Press Service*, February 1962, p. 47.

5 International Bank, *op. cit.*, p. 19.

6 Report to Petrobras by Mr. W. Link, Head of Exploration 1954–60, August 1960. See *Petroleum Press Service*, February 1961, pp. 47–48.

7   For an analysis of the Soviet Union's motives see P. R. Odell, 'Impact on the West of Growing Russian Oil Exports', *The Times*, 19th and 21st December 1961 and 'Russia in the Oil World', *New Statesman*, 23rd February 1962.

8   V. I. Veits, L. A. Melentieu and M. A. Styrikovich, 'Principles of Compiling Energy Balances in the U.S.S.R.'   A Paper presented to the World Power Conference, Madrid 1960, p. 7.

9   *Ibid.*, p. 9.

10   P. R. Odell, *op. cit.*

PART II

THE PATTERN
OF
WORLD OIL DEMAND

CHAPTER 4

The Pattern of Oil Consumption

We have already examined in Part I the overall role that demand for oil plays in determining the expansion of the world's proven reserves of petroleum and also how, to some degree, the pattern of production changes according to the differential development of demand in various parts of the world. It can be seen very clearly, for example, that the increasingly intensive use of oil in the Soviet Union under the impact of a rapidly expanding economy and a change-over from the use of coal to the use of oil has led to the decision to develop oil production more intensively in the U.S.S.R. in recent years than in most of the rest of the world, so that the share of Soviet output in the world total has increased from 6 to 13 per cent. in the decade 1950–60 and is still increasing at about the same rate. It would, however, be unwise to look always for direct relationships in growth between production and consumption on a regional basis, as this would mean discounting the impact of some of the political and organizational factors that were also shown in Part I to contribute significantly to determining the pattern of production.

On the other hand, examination of the regional variations in demand as a determinant of the patterns of production should not form the sole, or even the main, reason for including a section on the demand for petroleum in a text concerned with the economic geography of the industry. While analyses of patterns of production appear to have been recognized as the central theme of studies in economic geography, it is difficult to see the justification for the much more limited treatment of patterns of consumption. Certainly with a commodity as ubiquitous and as important as oil, the patterns of consumption are as susceptible of geographical analysis in their own right

59

as are the patterns of production. In fact, with petroleum the geography of consumption offers a much more effective guide to the stage of development of an economy than does the geography of production. It can also have a much greater impact on the regional differentiation of landscape. The impact of petroleum production on a landscape may be restricted to the temporary derricks, the well head structures, the collecting lines, a terminal and the housing and service facilities for a limited number of staff. Oil consumption, on the other hand, often brings with it the provision of refining and petrochemical industries, general industrialization, the growth of extensive and intensive means of transport and the huge agglomerations of population that are an inevitable result of such developments.

The economic geographer, therefore, looking at the oil industry cannot merely treat the pattern of consumption as a factor determining the pattern of supply, important though this relationship is. The pattern of consumption, in relation to the pattern of supply, is also of significance in explaining the changing location of the refinery industry and the associated movements of crude oil and products. (These aspects of the world oil industry will be examined in the next part of this book.) In addition, the pattern of consumption itself has to be described and explanations for its regional differentiation have to be sought. It is this aspect of the oil industry that forms the subject matter of this part of the book.

Petroleum can be neither easily nor cheaply stored but capacity to produce can be relatively easily restricted (in the physical sense) by 'capping' the wells whose output is not required. Thus production in any given year (or any other period) will be adjusted to the overall level of demand. The relationship will not, of course, be an exact one for several reasons. Some governments, particularly those of countries which are dependent on petroleum imports for their continued survival as industrial nations (and this includes most of the countries of Western Europe), insist on an adequate strategic stockpile of crude oil or petroleum products. This stockpile is often expressed in terms of so many days' or weeks' supplies and thus from year to year as consumption increases so the stockpile—in part provided by the marketing companies which will not show it as a sale until it finally leaves their tanks—must also increase.

Individual companies must also make allowances for seasonal or other variations in demand and provide themselves with commercial reserves for such eventualities. Stocks at any given calendar date will obviously vary from year to year depending on what eventualities there have been or, perhaps, what are anticipated, and this too will affect the relationship between supply and apparent consumption. For example, stocks at 31 December 1961, in the United States were about 4 million tons higher than those of a year earlier.[1] Companies may also experience some imbalance between their refineries' out-turn of products and the development of demand, and additional storage may have to be sought for the surplus if the situation cannot be resolved by international transactions designed to eliminate the difficulties, particularly between associated companies of the same Group. At the time of the Suez crisis, for example, demand for gasoline in the United Kingdom was severely curtailed by the introduction of a rationing scheme. So successful, however, was the combined government-industry plan for getting crude to this country, in spite of the closure of the Suez Canal and the pipelines through Syria, that the refineries were able to work at almost normal levels of production, thus ensuring that there were no shortages of oil for industry and commerce. The gasoline fractions could not, however, find a market because of rationing and, in spite of a movement of some of the surplus to the United States, stocks in Britain were gradually built up until every available tank was full.[2]

Certain competitive conditions can also produce embarrassing surpluses of gasoline. This is seen in the United States, where in response to imbalance between fuel oil and gasoline consumption and the higher per unit return on sales of the latter, refinery yields of gasoline have been increased by various technological developments and from additional capacity that has been built. Together the larger refinery capacity and the higher yield of gasoline per barrel of crude have resulted in an increase in gasoline capacity much in excess of the growth in demand. As no company wishes to have expensive capital equipment unused or underused and as all companies feel that they can do better than the industry as a whole in increasing sales, more gasoline than is required by the market (which is relatively inelastic to price changes) is produced and thus stocks rise.[3]

Another factor which produces an excess of production over consumption occurs in a period of rising demand when new facilities are continually being brought on stream (the normal situation to date in the oil industry). The pipelines from the field to the coast have to be filled with oil; the storage tanks at the export terminal have to be filled to ensure that supplies are always available for incoming tankers; the tankers themselves may take up to several weeks to carry their cargoes to the consuming countries, where again there may be some delay before the oil is refined and eventually consumed. Thus a period of several months may elapse between new production being achieved and consumption of the new oil actually taking place.

With these relatively minor provisos, however, it is possible to equate the demand for products with the supply of oil. In 1960 world consumption of petroleum fuels was about 900 million metric tons, with the balance of oil production going to stocks as noted above, and to non-energy uses such as the chemical feedstocks, bitumen, lubricating oils and other minor products such as waxes. In the analysis of the pattern of consumption these latter uses of petroleum will not be taken into account as they are infrequently of importance in their own right and as they involve special considerations. The inclusion of chemical feedstocks, for example, would involve a study of the chemical industry and thus widen the scope of this book to a very large extent.

Figure 4 illustrates the distribution of the consumption of petroleum fuels in 1960. As with the pattern of petroleum production the most significant feature is the dominant position of the United States, which consumes over 400 million tons, almost 45 per cent. of the world total. However, it should be noted that the share of the United States is falling quite significantly as a result of the much lower rate of increase in the demand for petroleum there than in most other parts of the world. In the decade 1950–60 petroleum demand in the United States increased at an average annual rate of only 4·3 per cent., compared with a rate of increase outside the

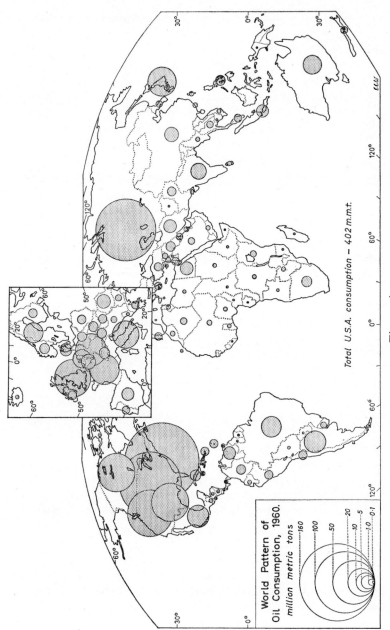

World Pattern of
Oil Consumption, 1960.
million metric tons

160
100
50
20
10
5
1.0
0.1

Total U.S.A. consumption – 402 m.m.t.

Figure 4

United States at least twice as great.   Moreover, the rate of increase in the United States is slackening even more than the figure for the last decade suggests.   In 1960 the rate of increase was down to 2·4 per cent. (compared with over 10 per cent. in the rest of the world) and in 1961 demand was only a little over 1 per cent. ahead of the previous year.

Western Europe is the second largest consuming area with a total demand in 1960 of about 166 million tons.   Five of the world's ten largest consuming countries (excluding the United States and the Soviet Union) are in this area.   These are the United Kingdom, with a consumption of almost 40 million tons; Western Germany and France, each using almost 30 million tons of oil; Italy, which consumed 20 million tons and Sweden which consumed over 11 million.   Since 1950 consumption in Western Europe has been increasing very rapidly, with an average annual rate of increase of almost 14 per cent.   The incremental demand each year in Western Europe has, in fact, for the last few years exceeded the additional amounts of oil sold in the United States.   In 1960 the additional 23 million tons of oil sold in Western Europe was only about 5 million tons less than the additional quantities sold in the whole of the remainder of the non-communist world.   This growing significance of the Western European oil market has, of course, had an important impact on those producing areas which are particularly well suited to supply it.   North Africa and the Middle East are in the most favourable locations in this respect, and the rapid expansion and the buoyancy of their Western European outlets has certainly been one of the main factors that has led to continued investment designed to secure increases in productive capacity throughout this period.   The Soviet Union is in a similarly favourable position and this will be further enhanced when the massive forty-inch pipeline from the Volga-Urals fields through to Eastern Europe and points on the Baltic and the East European/West European border is completed in 1963.   The Soviet Union plans to put almost 10 million tons of oil a year for Western Europe through this line, which will significantly reduce the costs of transporting the oil (it will replace a longer haul by pipeline, barge or rail and tanker from the Black Sea ports) and hence further improve the competitive position of Soviet oil in this market.

The communist group of countries provides the third major region of oil consumers and, as in Western Europe, it is a rapidly growing market for petroleum products. Though official figures of oil consumption are not available (they seem to be regarded as confidential by the governments concerned), it appears that in the decade from 1950 to 1960 demand increased from 50 to 132 million tons. Of the total about five-sixths (110 million tons in 1960) are consumed in the Soviet Union itself. No other communist country at the moment consumes more than 7 million tons—the approximate figure for China with its 600 million people.

Almost all the other significant oil consuming nations are in the Western Hemisphere. Canada is fourth only to the United States, the Soviet Union and the United Kingdom with a consumption of almost 40 million tons. It was, in fact, only in 1961 that consumption in Britain exceeded that of Canada, but as the Canadian market is now expanding only slowly (a mere 2 per cent. increase in 1960) and is not expected to increase by more than an average for the next few years of 4 per cent. per annum, the gap between consumption in the United Kingdom and that in Canada will gradually widen. It seems unlikely that Canada will be displaced from its position behind Britain in the table of oil consumption for several years, although a further relative decline eventually seems inevitable.

Mexico, Argentina and Brazil are ninth, tenth and eleventh in the table of consumption, with a total use of almost 40 million tons in 1960, divided almost equally among the three countries. In Latin America as a whole, where 65 million tons were used in 1960, consumption in the post-war period increased at more than 10 per cent. per annum until 1957, when worsening economic conditions curbed the rate of expansion. It is not expected that the increase in consumption will rise much above 7 per cent. per year in the next decade—a relatively low rate of increase compared with those expected in the other developing regions of the world.

In the whole of Africa, Asia and Australasia consumption of petroleum products exceeded 10 million tons in 1960 only in Japan, which is in fact close behind Western Germany and France in its use of oil—some 22 million tons. Increases in consumption in Japan have been even greater than those in the leading Western European consuming countries. Consumption in 1960 was over 38 per cent. ahead of that of 1959 and over the whole of the period 1950–60 the average annual rate of increase has been more than 25 per cent. Japanese economic planners now estimate that consumption in 1970 will be three times as great as that for 1960. However, although with the exception of Japan, the level of consumption in these areas of the world is very low, the rates of increase in oil demand have been relatively high and are expected to continue in the same way. In the Middle East, for example, the use of oil has been rising at the rate of 17 per cent. since 1950 but still totals only about 20 million tons. In South-East Asia and the Far East (excluding Japan and the communist countries) total consumption in 1960 was over 25 million tons and is also rising rapidly. Finally, despite their small populations, consumption in Australia and New Zealand has reached a total of more than 10 million tons and is increasing at the moment by about 1 million tons each year.

The variation in oil demand from country to country is, of course, in part simply a reflection of their differing sizes and, more particularly, their differing populations. Most of the world's most populous countries are numbered among the leading petroleum consumers. The United States and the Soviet Union, third and first in the world order of size respectively and both with a population exceeding 180 million are, as we have seen, far ahead as the world's two most important oil consuming countries. Other populous countries, including the United Kingdom, France, Western Germany, Japan and Brazil, are also numbered among the leading oil consumers. The impact of a country's size and population, however, has only a limited application in determining the level of oil demand. This will be clearly appreciated from the fact that the two countries with the largest populations—China and India—are small consumers of petroleum products. China, with over 600 million people and an area of over 4 million square miles consumes only some 7 million tons of oil per year. This is little more than the consumption in Switzerland with an area of less than 16,000 square miles and a population of only 4·5 million. India, with its population of over 450 million,

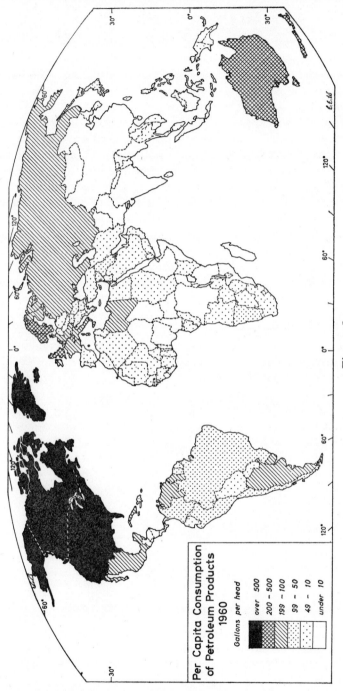

Per Capita Consumption
of Petroleum Products
1960

Gallons per head

over 500
200 – 500
199 – 100
99 – 50
49 – 10
under 10

Figure 5

consumes only 9 million tons of oil—significantly less than Sweden which has a population only one-twentieth as great.

In order to eliminate the effect of population differences between countries, the *per capita* consumption of petroleum products throughout the world must be examined.   The world pattern of consumption on this basis is shown in Figure 5. This brings out clearly the wide variations in the level of *per capita* demand for petroleum products.   At one end of the scale is the United States, where consumption is of the order of 630 imperial gallons per head, and at the other end is China, with an estimated consumption level of only two gallons per head.   Between these two extreme values there exist almost as many levels of *per capita* consumption as there are countries but in Figure 5 several broad divisions are shown. The United States and Canada are in a category by themselves, (except for the sparsely inhabited countries of Greenland and Iceland), but are followed by a group of countries—mainly in Western Europe, but also including Australia and New Zealand —where consumption lies between 200 and 500 gallons per head.   Included in the third category are most of the remaining countries of Western Europe, the U.S.S.R. and Czechoslovakia and several countries in Latin America.*   Most of the countries in Latin America, however, together with all but a few of the African and South-East Asian countries fall into the three groups using less than 100 gallons of petroleum products per head.

The factors that determine the *per capita* use of oil from country to country will be examined in the next chapter.

REFERENCES

1   The Chase Manhattan Bank, New York. *Monthly Review of the Petroleum Situation*, January, 1962.
2   From information provided by one of the refining companies in the United Kingdom.
3   The Chase Manhattan Bank, New York. *Op. cit.*, November 1961.

* Some countries such as Kuwait, Bahrain, Netherlands Antilles, etc., fall into this group because they have small populations combined with the existence of important export refineries using large quantities of fuel in the refining processes.

CHAPTER 5

Factors Determining
the Pattern of Oil Demand

The level of *per capita* oil consumption within a country is a function of two related considerations. The first is the ability or otherwise of oil to compete with other sources of primary energy—viz.: coal, natural gas, hydro-electricity and nuclear power—in relative prices which may, of course, be affected by other than commercial considerations—in particular, by government intervention in the fuel economy—and in convenience of use in processes for which oil provides an alternative source to the others for power or heat. The second main consideration determining the *per capita* use of oil is the degree of economic development that has been attained. It is such development, measured by the intensity of industrialization, including transport facilities, which, to a large degree, determines the overall level of energy use, to which, as already indicated, oil consumption is related.

The existence of a *general* relationship between levels of energy consumption and levels of economic activity has been shown in investigations carried out in many countries over the last thirty-five years.[1] Attempts, however, to establish *precise* relationships lead to serious difficulties and the results are subject to reservations. In the first place there are difficulties in defining and quantifying both energy consumption and economic activity each in terms of a common unit. For example, the output of hydro-electricity can be measured either in terms of the coal equivalent of the electricity actually produced or in terms of the amount of coal that would have been needed to produce the same amount of electricity in a thermal station. If the latter method is selected, the conversion factor used will vary both from time to time and from place to place to take account of the varying efficiencies of thermal power stations in converting coal or oil into electricity.[2]   The difficulties of quantifying in monetary terms the output of goods and services—as, for example, in those economies with a large subsistence sector—and of making international comparisons with all the problems attendant upon the use of a multitude of currencies are set out clearly in the national income studies by the United Nations.[3]

Secondly, the relationship between the two variables differs at different stages of economic development.   In a dormant economy little commercial energy is used, as people at the subsistence level have no monetary income with which to purchase fuel for heat and light but depend rather on the use of material—such as wood and dung, etc.—which can be collected or grown.   In such an economy the interchange of goods and people is at a minimum and hence the demand for transport is extremely limited.   As the initial steps towards economic development are undertaken, however, the use of energy rises quickly with the establishment of energy intensive industries such as power, cement and, later, iron and steel. Such industries lead to a rapid expansion in the demand for transport with its inevitable energy needs.   Industrialization and urbanization give rise to conditions in which increasing numbers of the population are unable to seek their own fuel requirements and they thus become dependent on purchases of kerosene, coal, electricity and gas.   At a later stage of economic development, as greater percentages of the national product arise from industries and services which are light energy users, the rate of increase in the consumption of energy falls away.[4]

A third complicating factor arises from the increasing efficiency in the use of energy which occurs in an economy where technological developments are commonplace and in which entrepreneurs are constantly seeking means of reducing their costs of production in order to gain an advantage over their competitors.   The widespread replacement of steam by diesel traction on the railways is a significant example of such a development, for in certain circumstances—notably shunting operations—1 ton of diesel fuel (which has the equivalent in heat value of about 1·5 tons of coal) can save up to 7 tons of coal. It has been estimated that in the United States the policy of rail dieselization, now virtually complete, provides an annual saving of 50 million tons of coal.[5] Of greater significance are the developments that have taken place in the efficiencies of power stations. In the United States in 1920, it took 3·00 lbs. of coal to produce 1 kilowatt hour of electricity; in 1930 it took only 1·60 lbs.; in 1940, 1·34 lbs.; in 1950 1·19 lbs.; and today less than 0·90 lbs. with the prospects of further improvements by 1980 to only 0·76 lbs. In the United Kingdom the average efficiency of power stations has increased from 21·7 per cent. in 1950–51 to 26·8 per cent. in 1960–61. The most efficient, moreover, are now being operated at efficiencies of almost 35 per cent.[6]

A fourth complication is introduced by the variations in the trading regimes of different countries. If the country concerned produces goods for export which have involved the consumption of more energy than the goods it imports, *per capita* consumption of energy in the country will be higher than that in another country with the same standard of economic development but with a contrasting trading regime. Thus Belgium/Luxembourg, with its manufacture and export of iron and steel produced by highly energy intensive processes, has a *per capita* consumption of energy more than 50 per cent. greater than that of Denmark, whose industries are generally not energy intensive, even though the two countries quite obviously are at about the same stage of economic development and, in fact, both have a *per capita* national income of about £350.

Because of these several complicating factors it is obviously impossible to establish any precise and accurate correlation between national income and the use of energy. In any case a further detailed discussion of the relationship would appear to be inappropriate for a general explanation of national differences in oil consumption, which is the prime aim of this chapter. With this aim in mind, however, Table 3 has been drawn up to indicate the broad relationship that is generally acceptable.

In this Table, forty-one countries are listed in order of their energy consumption *per capita* (based on their use of different fuels, converted [7] into the equivalent of hard coal of 12,400 B.T.U.'s per lb.). Consumption, it will be seen, ranges from

TABLE 3

PER CAPITA ENERGY CONSUMPTION AND NATIONAL INCOME

Country	Energy Consumption (lbs. of coal equivalent)	National Income (£'s)
United States	3642	815
* Canada	2581	550
United Kingdom	2237	386
Belgium/Luxembourg	1804	343
Australia	1773	443
Western Germany	1660	332
Iceland	1656	279
* Sweden	1590	519
Denmark	1282	380
Netherlands	1282	295
* Norway	1241	343
Venezuela	1163	313
South Africa	1096	134
* France	1092	338
* Austria	991	230
Ireland	915	180
* New Zealand	901	480
* Switzerland	881	478
* Finland	744	296
Puerto Rico	663	223
Israel	575	224
* Italy	540	186
Japan	530	117
Argentina	486	135
Mexico	460	100
Cyprus	377	116
Spain	373	93
Malta	249	132
Jamaica	240	128
Rhodesias and Nyasaland	237	60
Colombia	231	108
Portugal	165	79
Turkey	108	64
* Costa Rica	87	103
Ecuador	80	55
Guatemala	66	56
Ceylon	48	43
Paraguay	40	37
Kenya, Uganda, Tanganyika	36	25
Thailand	28	33
Burma	25	18

Sources: Energy Consumption—U.N. Statistical Papers, Series J, No. 5.   National Income *per capita*—Estimated from 1960 figures of national income, population and exchange rates in U.N. Monthly Bulletin of Statistics, May 1962.

* See footnote on p. 73.

3642 lbs. per head in the United States down to 25 lbs. in Burma. In the third column are shown the estimates of *per capita* national income for each of these countries.[8] It will be readily apparent from the table that the relationship between energy consumption and the national income is a close one, although there are several obvious disparities between the two series. Such disparities are generally understandable in the light of the previous observations on the difficulties of establishing strictly comparable data.*

Thus, expressed in general terms, one can accept the thesis that the higher the stage of economic development that has been achieved, the greater the use of energy. It is this general relationship between economic development and energy use which sets the pattern for oil consumption, which, world-wide, now provides about one-third of the total energy consumed.† The overall significance of petroleum in world energy use and its relationship to other sources of energy in the period 1920–60 are shown in Figure 6. Petroleum products provided under 10 per cent. of total energy demand in 1920; their share increased to 20 per cent. by 1935 and to almost 30 per cent. in the next fifteen years. Since 1950 their share has increased more slowly, but they now stand at about one-third of the total and it is expected that they will meet about 40 per cent. of total energy demand by 1970.[9]

This historical pattern in the development of the use of petroleum suggests that oil is well able to compete with the other sources of energy and most particularly with solid fuel (mainly coal), whose share in total energy consumption has declined from 88 per cent. in 1920 to only 50 per cent. at the present time. The competitive process between different sources of energy works itself out in different ways in different

---

* In particular, the difficulties which arise in comparing hydro-electricity with other sources of energy are apparent. The United Nations statistics convert hydro-electricity to coal equivalent in terms of the heat value of the electricity produced. However, as the electricity produced is used much more efficiently than other sources of energy, this method tends to understate the energy used in countries with significant hydro-electricity output (these countries are marked with an asterisk in Table 3). Had the alternative method of converting hydro-electricity been used (see p. 69), total energy used in these countries would have appeared to be much greater. For example, *per capita* use in New Zealand would have appeared as 1460 lbs. compared with 910 lbs. in the Table.

† Excluding minor sources of energy such as wood, vegetable waste, dung, etc. These are, however, locally significant in certain economies.

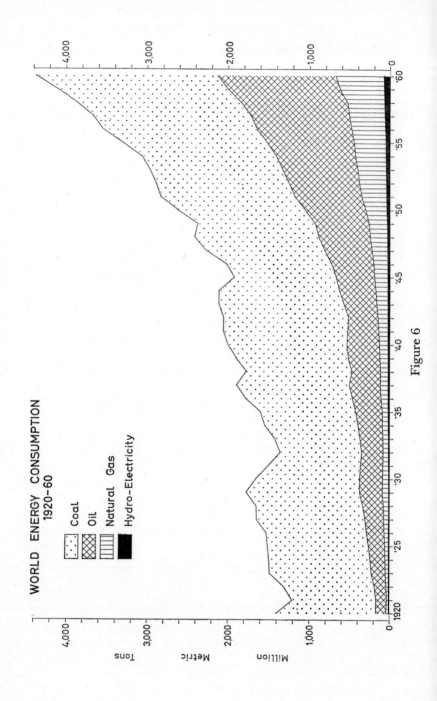

WORLD ENERGY CONSUMPTION
1920–60

Coal
Oil
Natural Gas
Hydro-Electricity

Million Metric Tons

Figure 6

countries, and several significant examples will be examined later in this chapter. First of all, however, it should be noted that of all the sources of energy, petroleum has the broadest based non-competitive markets. In such markets consumption will be related directly to the development of the sectors of the economy concerned and the degree of technical advance, which generally aims to reduce the amount of energy required to do a given job. Of greatest significance in this respect is the use of oil in transport, where, with two exceptions noted below, it is virtually immune from competition from other energy sources.

The first exception arises from the continued use of coal-fired steam engines for rail transport notably in countries such as the United Kingdom and Germany where suitable coal is available and where much of the railways' business is concerned with the movement of coal. Even in these countries, however, there is a strong trend towards alternative means of traction because of the great economies in running costs that can thereby be secured* and because of greater public acceptance of diesel and electric motive power. Thus, in the United Kingdom the use of coal by the railways has declined from 14·9 million tons in 1945 to only 7·7 million tons in 1961, while in the same period the use of oil has increased from a negligible quantity to 290,000 tons. In countries, such as Argentina, where the railways are unable to finance capital improvements because of rigid government control over fares and tariffs and excessive expenditure on labour which is surplus to requirements, the provision of capital from international and United States sources is being employed in part to convert the motive power from steam to diesel traction. Capital for this purpose seems likely to be available for as many developing countries as wish to convert their railways from steam to diesel, and the only major countries which seem likely to continue to depend on coal-fired steam engines are India and Communist China.

The second exception to the immunity of oil from competition in transport arises from the use of electricity for rail traction and for some urban transport (trams and trolley buses). The

---

* This, of course, arises not only from economies in fuel (see p. 70) but also from the higher utilization obtained with deisel and electric locomotives. The proportions of time spent 'off-line' by steam, diesel and electric locomotives respectively can be stated by the ratio 25 : 8 : 5.

electricity used may be, and in fact generally is, generated from coal, natural gas or hydro power rather than from oil. However, rail electrification is a highly capital intensive development and is likely, therefore, to be restricted, first, to those countries in which capital is readily available (for example, the Soviet Union, France, the United Kingdom), and, secondly, within these countries to the relatively few main lines and suburban services where the density of traffic is sufficient to justify the expenditure.*   Thus, the ability of other sources of energy to compete with oil in providing motive power seems likely to continue to be at a relatively low level and their gains from rail electrification seem certain to be more than offset by their losses from the dieselization of steam services.

For all other means of transport oil products have no competitors.   The expansion of motor transport for the carriage of passengers and goods is thus of particular significance in stimulating the demand for oil.   In the United States gasoline accounts for over 40 per cent. of total petroleum consumption, and this very sizeable proportion of total petroleum demand will be affected only by the rate at which the market for motor vehicles expands and by any changes in the amount of fuel used by each vehicle—a function of engine technology and annual mileage.   The significance of these latter factors is shown by the situation in the United States, where, although the number of vehicles will continue to increase, improvements in engine efficiency and a declining annual mileage per vehicle (coupled with an increasing preference for smaller cars) seem likely to limit the increasing use of gasoline and hence have an important overall effect on the demand for petroleum products.   Outside the United States—but excluding the Soviet bloc, where there are not the same moves to 'motorization'—the number of motor vehicles has been growing at a rate of about 12 per cent. per annum in recent years, and it is expected that this high rate of growth will be very nearly maintained during the rest of the decade.   This development has been, and still is, particularly significant in Western Europe, where since the early 1950s

* There are also certain countries, such as Switzerland and Norway, where the availability of cheap hydro-electric power has made the electrification of railways possible on a wider scale.

there has been a break-through into the establishment of a mass market for motor cars and where, under the impact of technological, economic and political factors coupled with the growth of systems of motor roads, there has been a great advance in the use of motor transport for carrying freight. Table 4 indicates the growth in the number of cars and lorries in several of the major European countries since the Second World War.

TABLE 4

MOTOR VEHICLES IN
WESTERN EUROPEAN COUNTRIES, 1946–61

(figures in thousands)

Country	Cars				Lorries			
	1946	*1951*	*1956*	*1961*	*1946*	*1951*	*1956*	*1961*
United Kingdom	1807	2433	3981	6114	572	955	1201	1490
France	997	1382	3351	6158	500*	883	1285	1684
West Germany	73*	796	2204	5167	67*	523	671	791
Italy	150	426	1040	2444	136	243	375	473
Sweden	138	313	735	1194	60	91	111	122
Belgium	86	304	537	820	91	151	144	186
Holland	47	157	327	603	47	81	123	183
Denmark	100	123	249	470	34	64	108	185

Source: The Motor Industry of Great Britain 1962; Society of Motor Manufacturers and Traders Ltd., except where indicated with *. These are from Automobile Facts and Figures 1947.

This rapid growth in the number of motor vehicles has been one of the main factors in the expanding market for petroleum products in Western Europe, where motor gasoline and diesel oil (partly used for automotive purposes) now account for about 45 per cent. of total petroleum consumption.

Similarly, transport by air and by sea is fuelled almost exclusively by petroleum products, with the few remaining coal-burning ships gradually being eliminated. Thus, as both ocean and air transport continue to expand with the rise in international trade and the growth in foreign travel, the demand for petroleum products for these purposes will also expand. For the oil industry a very important development in air transport has been the change-over to turbo-prop and turbo-jet aircraft by both military and civil operators. In consequence sales of aviation gasoline have ceased to expand,* whereas sales of kerosene have increased at a much faster rate than was anticipated a few years ago. In the United States, for example, where the demand for kerosene had stagnated for almost thirty years at about 5 per cent. of total petroleum products consumption, there have been increases in demand for this cut of the barrel of the order of 12 per cent. per annum in the years since 1958. For shipping, the possibilities of nuclear propulsion have been fully investigated in recent years. However, even apart from any question of safety considerations, it has now been demonstrated that nuclear propulsion is uneconomic compared with conventional methods and is likely to remain so for many years. Thus, the British Government announced in 1961 that the plans for the construction of an experimental nuclear powered merchant ship were to be abandoned although further research into the problems of nuclear propulsion would continue.[10] It therefore seems that nuclear power for shipping will for some time ahead be restricted mainly to military use, for which the long cruising periods without refuelling that are possible with nuclear propulsion outweigh the considerations of the higher cost involved.

In examining the non-competitive uses of petroleum products it should be borne in mind that though these products are most economically made by refining crude oil, this is not the only way in which they can be made available. The possibilities of extracting oil products from oil shales and the Athabasca tar sands have been previously noted (page 10), and a growing quantity of gasoline is also being extracted from 'wet' natural gas in the United States and Canada and is competing success-fully with the product distilled from crude petroleum. These developments might, however, be viewed as extensions of the petroleum industry for most natural gas production is either associated with crude oil production or is produced by companies with their main interests in oil. Similarly, most experiments on the oil shales and the tar sands have generally

---

* This is the case except in certain parts of the world where, for reasons of economy, local air transport continues to use fully depreciated piston-engined planes such as the ubiquitous Dakota.

been carried out by oil companies. Petroleum products, however, can also be made from coal, though the process is generally unprofitable at the present level of oil prices. Only in the Union of South Africa are oil products produced from coal on anything more than an experimental basis. It is possible at Sasolburg in the Orange Free State only because of the very low pit-head price of coal (which is charged to the works at a cash cost of less than 4s. per short ton exclusive of interest and depreciation) [11] and the high cost of transporting petroleum products from the coastal refineries and ocean depots to the centres of inland consumption in the Rand. Such favourable conditions do not exist anywhere else in the world, yet even in South Africa it has been only within the past few years that SASOL—the state enterprise charged with producing oil products from coal—has been able to work at a profit. For the present, therefore, the likelihood of oil products being made in any quantity from anything apart from crude oil is fairly remote, although it is worth noting reports that certain United States oil companies are buying interests in coal mining, presumably as an insurance against future developments.

Finally, the possibilities of the use of fuel cells * for road and rail transport should be mentioned. The potentialities for such a development have obviously been recognized by petroleum interests, for some of the leading oil companies are in the forefront of research in this field. Success in this direction would introduce a competitive element into the presently non-competitive uses of petroleum products, and as these account for over 50 per cent. of the total market in North America and for over 30 per cent. in the rest of the non-communist world, the significance for the oil industry and the world pattern of petroleum demand should not be underestimated.

Except for the exclusive uses for petroleum products noted in the preceding paragraphs and for certain very energy

* A device which will develop electricity directly from the chemical reaction of oxygen with hydrogen or hydrocarbons. Unlike a battery which is either discarded as the active material is used up or intermittently recharged, a fuel cell is continuously fed with oxygen and the chosen fuel. The technical feasibility of powering vehicles by this means has been demonstrated, but problems such as cost and the size of the unit remain to be solved before its commercial potentiality can be realized.

intensive processes which can only be carried out economically if hydro-electricity is available, practically all needs for fuel and power can be met by two or more of the primary sources of energy.

Recent technological developments in the iron and steel industry seem likely partly to eliminate the remaining important non-competitive market for coal—the production of metal-lurgical coke previously essential for the manufacture of iron. Though most blast furnaces already in existence and most of those which are to be built in the existing major iron and steel producing areas will probably continue to use the traditional method of iron production, this will be because of the competi-tive advantage that coal has in such areas, many of which are coalfield located, or because of the ties that exist between the two industries, or because of the skills locally available for the traditional process or because of the need to employ capital assets that have already been constructed. The new methods of fuel oil injection into the blast furnaces (with the alternative injection of either natural gas or powdered coal) which reduce the need for coke by up to 30 per cent. are technically equally suited to produce iron, and there is evidence that such methods in fact reduce the overall costs of production. The methods, therefore, may be expected to win favour in areas where iron production is to be established or expanded and where supplies of suitable coal are either not available or are less readily available than alternative supplies of oil or natural gas.

Such possibilities may be seen in Venezuela where the World Bank Mission called in to advise on economic develop-ment, has recommended that a full investigation be made into the possibilities of using some of the country's available supplies of oil or natural gas (much of which is flared off because it cannot be utilized) to produce the iron at the new iron and steel plant at Guayana rather than to proceed with the develop-ment at high cost of some nearby coal reserves of dubious quality for metallurgical processes.[12]

Similarly in Brazil where production of steel is planned to increase from its present level of 2·5 million tons to over 5 million tons by 1965, the use of more cheaply transported fuel oil rather than metallurgical coke, which cannot be produced in sufficient quantities from the poor and high cost

Brazilian coal, seems to offer a chance that the plan for steel will be fulfilled.

In Argentina, too, plans to increase the capacity of the steel industry from under 1 million tons in 1962 to a level of 4·5 million tons per annum by 1965 seemed unlikely to be fulfilled in view of the shortage of suitable coking coal and the impossibility of importing supplies and transporting them to the interior locations of the iron and steel plants at a cost which would make production economical. However, Argentina's rapidly expanding production of oil and natural gas and the development of an adequate pipeline system to take it to the main industrial areas should go a long way towards solving this problem.

Thus, in much of industry, in the production of gas and electricity and in commercial and residential use the consumption of oil depends on its ability to compete with the other major sources of primary energy. The main factors that have to be taken into account are the physical availability of the alternative sources of energy, their prices in relation to their different efficiencies in use, their relative suitability and convenience in various end-uses and—often most important of all—the attitude of national governments to the several possibilities of meeting the energy requirements of the country. The way in which these considerations work themselves out will be illustrated by reference to specific instances in different parts of the world, as the pattern is not explicable in terms of any general principles but must rather be explained on an 'ad hoc' basis from country to country and from region to region within a country—even in those very much smaller than the United States or the Soviet Union, where regional differences in the competitiveness of different fuels would be expected.

United States

Few countries are endowed with as wide a variety of energy resources as the United States, which has currently recoverable reserves of coal of the order of 950,000 million tons; reserves of crude oil potentially available for future recovery of the order of 75,000 million tons together with shale oil resources considerably larger than this; known reserves of natural gas equal to more than twenty years' supply and with further supplies of gas most probably in association with the ultimate reserves of oil; and a hydro-electricity potential more than three times greater than the capacity currently developed. Moreover, the energy resources are widely distributed throughout the country with each of the major consuming regions having a large part of its energy requirements locally available, with the exception of the major deficit area of the north-east. With such a wide resource base and with a system of government ideologically committed to the market economy with its theoretical base lying in freedom of consumer choice, it would seem logical that the level of oil consumption would be related to its ability to compete with other fuels for the favours of the consumers. This is true in part but, as will be shown later, there are several factors which make the actual position a little more complicated than might be expected.

Even as recently as 1946 the United States' economy was still essentially based on coal, which then provided almost half of the country's total energy requirements. Coal probably accounted for about two-thirds of the energy used in the competitive sectors of the energy economy. The immediate post-war period was, however, a period of energy shortages and there were obviously large opportunities for oil and natural gas to fill the incremental demand from a rapidly growing economy. Since 1946 energy consumption has more than doubled but, whereas coal consumption has actually declined from over 500 to under 350 million tons, the consumption of natural gas has increased by 200 per cent. and that of petroleum by about 75 per cent. The share of each of these three main sources of energy in total consumption in the period since 1946 is shown in Table 5.

Thus, during this fifteen-year period oil has become the single most important source of energy as it has replaced coal in railway transport, in home heating and in industrial uses. Its gains in these competitive markets have, however, been much smaller than its increased use in markets where there was no competition, most notably in air and road transport. It has been estimated that between 1946 and 1958 about two-thirds of the increased consumption of oil has arisen in its own exclusive markets.[13] A much more important competitor of coal has in fact been natural gas, which has also taken markets which would otherwise have gone to oil. This in part reflects the construction of long distance gas pipelines from the major supply regions, enabling gas to be used in areas in which it had not been previously available. By 1961, with the completion of a line into the Pacific north-west, every state in the Union could take advantage of natural gas supplies.

TABLE 5

THE CONTRIBUTION OF MAJOR FUELS TO TOTAL
ENERGY CONSUMPTION IN THE UNITED STATES
1946–61

(in percentages)

Fuel	1946	1951	1956	1961
Coal	48	36	28	24
Oil	33	38	41	42
Natural Gas	15	22	26	29

Source: United States Bureau of Mines. Minerals Yearbook 1961, Vol. 2

Natural gas in the immediate post-war years also benefitted from the pricing policies adopted by the producers, for often the gas was viewed merely as a by-product of wells drilled for oil and its well-head price, therefore, tended to reflect only out-of-pocket expenses rather than its full share of the overall costs of exploration and development.[14] Were it not for the fact that the cost of transporting gas by pipeline is relatively high, the development of gas consumption could well have been greater. The activities of the Federal Power Commission —with the right to deny extensions of the use of natural gas into uses and areas where it is considered neither essential nor particularly advantageous—similarly restricted the expansion of natural gas developments although its control over well-head prices since 1954 and its regulation of pipeline operations have recently had an opposite effect. The work of this Commission is one of the factors—referred to earlier—which has complicated the manner in which energy consumption has expanded, so that it does not fully reflect the working out of the competitive process.

Oil production has been held back to less than the productive capacity of the industry would indicate to be possible. Capacity to produce is probably more than 500 million tons per annum, whereas the actual level of production is of the order of 350 million tons only. This is in part a reflection of the competition from natural gas, but is also an indication of the result of efforts made to maintain the price of oil in the United States at a level well above that in the world market. Thus in many of the producing areas of the United States production has been cut back to the level at which the output can be sold at a premium price. Little wonder, therefore, that oil's main headway in much of the post-war period has been in those markets where it has had no competition to meet.

The situation might have been different if sufficient lower-priced imports had been available to provide more effective competition with natural gas and to bring greater pressure to bear on oil prices in general. However, it was not until the late 1950s, with the development of an actual world surplus of oil aided by the low ocean freight rates for oil moving from the Middle East, that overseas oil producers started to push greater quantities of their crude and products into the American market, over and above the flow that had gradually developed in the post-war period to meet crude and product deficiences on the west coast and a deficiency of crude and residual fuel oil on the east coast.[15] The United States market was not, however, long left wide-open to cheaper supplies from abroad. In March 1959 the Eisenhower administration established mandatory control over oil imports (after 'voluntary' controls by the industry had proved ineffective) whereby imports were to be limited to the assessed gap between estimated domestic production and requirements. The programme was justified on security grounds: it was felt to be necessary in order to ensure the continuation of exploration for domestic oil in case future crises in the world's major producing areas or along the main transport routes cut off overseas supplies of oil. Whatever the justification for the programme, however, it is in essence an effective protective device for national fuel industries and, as such, is far removed from the much vaunted United States belief in the efficacy of free competition. The controls serve to protect the domestic oil industry (and, incidentally the domestic coal industry, particularly in its market for power generation in New England) by limiting the supply of oil and hence maintaining prices at a level at which increased domestic production is competitive. Because of the higher price level that has thus been maintained for oil products, natural gas can extend its markets even further and the coal industry has been able to keep and even to expand its market in certain areas of the country—notably the north-east coast, where competition from natural gas is at its weakest owing to the distance from the producing fields and where its main competition ought to come from cheap imported crude oil and products.

As a result of the inter-play of these factors, the growth in the consumption of petroleum in the United States has slackened even from the relatively low rate of increase of an average 4·3 per cent. per annum in the 1950s. Though economic expansion may be expected to continue throughout the 1960s, with a declared aim by the Kennedy administration of an annual increase in the Gross National Product in real terms of 4·5 per cent. per year, the outlook for increases in petroleum consumption is far from bright. (Forecasts of the future growth in consumption vary between 2·5 and 3·5 per cent. per annum.) In its non-competitive uses increases in demand will be restricted by the changeover to smaller and more economical cars, and in the other markets the industry will be faced by effective competition both from natural gas and from a resurgent coal industry, which is expected to make a come-back based on reduced costs of production and transport, lower prices and increasing demand, particularly from power stations. The inability of the petroleum industry to reduce its prices because of the insistence of the domestic producers, backed up by effective government support, that imports of cheaper oil be kept out seems to indicate that oil will win few new markets and may indeed be severely pressed to retain even those which it holds at the moment. Thus, in spite of the increasing affluence of the United States, which will probably result in its leaping even further ahead of the rest of the world (with the possible exceptions of the European Economic Community and the Soviet Union), one might expect world petroleum consumption to become less significantly oriented towards the United States, which by 1970 may be using little more than a third of total world consumption.

G

Western Europe

In contrast to the relatively weak competitive position of petroleum in the United States, petroleum products in Western Europe have, over the past decade, been making significant inroads into the essentially coal-based economy of the region. It has been the inability of coal to compete for the expanding energy markets, at first because of difficulties in increasing the supply of coal and more recently because of price considerations, together with the expanding non-competitive uses of oil, particularly in the automotive field, that has led to the rapid rate of increase in oil consumption noted earlier (see page 64). In Western Europe as a whole the share of oil in the total energy consumption has increased from 13 per cent. in 1950 to 30 per cent. by 1960.   The changes in the main countries over this period are shown in Table 6.

TABLE 6

OIL'S CONTRIBUTION TO TOTAL ENERGY
CONSUMPTION IN MAJOR WESTERN EUROPEAN
COUNTRIES 1950–60

(in millions of metric tons of coal equivalent)

Country	1950		1955		1960	
	Energy Consumption	Percentage of Oil	Energy Consumption	Percentage of Oil	Energy Consumption	Percentage of Oil
United Kingdom	222·9	9·5	254·5	13·6	259·0	24·1
West Germany	123·0	3·3	169·2	6·7	202·9	19·6
France	78·6	16·8	93·7	23·0	109·4	30·0
Italy	20·5	24·7	34·7	41·7	58·6	56·1
Sweden	15·0	34·5	19·9	57·7	26·1	71·4

Source: U.N. Statistical Papers—Series J.   Note that hydro-electricity is included in terms of the coal equivalent of the electricity actually produced, viz.: 1000 kWh = 0·125 tons coal.   See p. 69 and footnote on p. 73.

The general success of oil in expanding its share of the competitive markets in countries as dissimilar as those listed above both in their indigenous supplies of energy and in the kinds of economic policies their governments have followed, has arisen from two main sets of factors.   In the early years after the war, and even up to 1955, the demand for energy exceeded the supplies available. In particular the coal industry was unable to expand its output sufficiently quickly to match the demand. The growth of world oil supplies in this period was, therefore, very welcome and encouragement was given to the use of oil rather than of coal. Thus, in the United Kingdom the Government encouraged the building of power stations designed to burn oil and the conversion of coal-fired stations to oil-firing. In this way it was hoped that oil would replace the use of some 8 million tons of coal per annum. Many other European countries which had formerly relied on imported coal now found that supplies were unobtainable except at high cost from the United States, and they also proceeded with conversion to oil.

Since 1955 the post-war shortage of fuels has disappeared. An economic recession brought a check to rising energy demand and thereafter industrialists and others put energy costs under close scrutiny in an effort to reduce the costs of production so that exports might be made more competitive. Thus, increased efforts were made to find the cheapest energy supplies and to use energy more efficiently. In this situation the general tendency of coal prices to rise relative to those of oil led to the development of a marked preference for oil fuel over much of Western Europe. Since 1958 this preference has been strengthened by the falling away of oil prices under the impact of increased supplies both from new areas (for example, the Soviet Union and North Africa) and from new suppliers (such as United States companies with Venezuelan and other supplies surplus to their western hemisphere requirements) which had not formerly sought outlets in the European market. Petroleum fuels have thus gradually become competitive over a widening range of uses even in areas of Europe in close proximity to the coalfields. It has been estimated that by April 1961, only 30 per cent. of Britain's annual production of almost 200 million tons of coal was competitive with the ex-refinery price of fuel oil. In such a situation the conversion of power stations (in which use oil has no greater efficiency in use than coal and in which the question of cleanliness and convenience does not arise) from coal- to oil-firing in all areas except those in juxtaposition to the low-cost coal mines of the

East Midlands obviously became a possible development if the generating authority were to take only commercial factors into account. The imposition of a 2·2d. per gallon tax on fuel oil (equivalent to a tax of over £2 per ton—about 25 per cent. on the ex-refinery price) significantly altered the relationship in favour of coal so that over 95 per cent. of production now became competitive. In view, however, of the inevitability of rising costs in the coal industry,[16] and of the likelihood that the country will eventually secure cheaper supplies of oil as newcomers move in and thus upset the oligopoly of refining and marketing operations in this country, it would seem that this will prove no more than a temporary setback for oil in the process of securing additional outlets.

In many other parts of Europe the situation has already moved even more strongly in favour of oil because of the generally higher cost of coal production, and the lower prices for oil resulting from a greater degree of competition amongst oil suppliers and the existence of refinery capacity independent of the major international oil companies. As a result of these factors, oil prices have fallen well below the prices posted by the major companies. In Italy discounts of up to 62 cents a barrel (representing a cut of about 30 per cent.) off the posted price are reported as having been obtained on crude oil imported by independent refining companies. In Germany there have been discounts of 54 cents a barrel and discounts of between 30 and 40 per cent. have also been reported from Belgium. In the face of such competition the European coal industry has found great difficulty in maintaining its markets, let alone in securing a share of the incremental demand for energy.

In Germany the imposition of a fuel oil tax in 1960 designed to protect the coal industry was largely ineffective as, in general, the tax was absorbed by the suppliers and the prices to consumers were not raised. Thus, coal production in West Germany fell away from 153 million tons in 1956 to 142 million tons in 1961, when the industry was only working at 75 per cent. of capacity.* The situation has not yet been stabilized and a report [17] to the German government in 1962 suggested that

---

* Domestic coal production has been affected not only by competition from oil but also by imports of cheaper coal mainly from the United States.

production should be cut back to about 125 million tons by 1975.

In Belgium, the high cost mines have been unable to compete with oil and there have been many closures and an overall attempt at the rationalization of the industry. Production declined from a post-war peak of almost 30 million tons in 1957 to 21 million tons in 1961.

A similar situation has arisen even in Austria, where oil prices are higher as a result of the transport costs on imported products mainly obtained from refineries on the Italian Adriatic coast and in the Ruhr. Consumption of oil products rose at the expense of coal in spite of the imposition of a fuel oil tax in 1960. As a result coal output declined from 7 million tons in 1957 to 5·7 million tons in 1961. In spite of this significant fall in production, stocks of coal in 1961 rose to a level equal to about one-third of the annual output and the coal industry accumulated deficits of about £1 million per annum.

Thus, after rising to a post-war peak of about 600 million tons in 1957, European coal consumption fell away quite rapidly and by 1960, in view of increasing competition from oil, there appeared possibilities of the collapse of significant sectors of the industry, with accompanying social problems and the likelihood of greatly increased reliance on imported oil despite the political and supply risks entailed. The implications of this have perhaps been given the closest attention in West Germany, where the failure of fiscal measures to stabilize the situation has already been noted. The German government commissioned a full-scale enquiry into the problems of future demand for and supply of energy. This enquiry was commissioned in spite of the fact that the government has already had the benefit of a survey made by an American oil consultant, Mr. W. Levy, for the German Confederation of Industries.[18] Although essentially an 'oilman', Levy has argued in favour of protection of coal against fuel oil on the grounds that coal is at present uneconomic because fuel oil prices are abnormally low, thereby exerting a short-term competitive pressure which cannot be maintained in the future. He argued that this short-term pressure is sufficient to cause unnecessary and unwelcome long-term disruptions in coal-producing capacity and went on to recommend (to the consternation of the oil companies) that in order to prevent this development, actual energy prices should be geared to a more realistic long-term trend and that since fuel oil prices had deviated from this the immediate remedy should be to increase prices by additional taxation. Additionally, he suggested that the electricty generation market should be reserved to the coal industry in order to produce a growth sector for coal and to increase the security of electricity supply.

The report was attacked by the oil industry on the grounds that it would increase the price of energy and thus make national output less competitive with that from countries, such as Japan and Italy, using the cheapest fuels available. The industry also pointed out that the recommendations would remove the incentive to rationalization in the coal industry, which because of rising costs would not, it claimed, be a viable competitor with fuel oil in the foreseeable future. However, even though the report may not have presented all the implications arising from its recommendations, it did indicate the kind of action that governments in coal-producing countries would have to take if they wish to maintain the output of coal at levels sufficiently high to minimize social problems and to avoid great reliance on imported energy.

In the United Kingdom, the decision to convert all dual-fired power stations using oil back to coal (in spite of the protests of the electricity authorities), the refusal to accept supplies of Soviet oil which would weaken the price structure and intensify competition, and the imposition of a fuel oil tax were all designed to offer a measure of protection to indigenous coal production or coincidentally had that effect. The major oil companies, in part probably because they show some appreciation of the difficulties facing the coal industry and recognize the need for security of energy supplies, in part because they wish to avoid even harsher government action against them at a later and perhaps more critical stage, and, in part because they probably wish to avoid an unduly rapid growth of demand for fuel oil, which gives a lower rate of return than other products and which could lead to imbalance in their refinery operations, would be not unhappy to see the power market reserved for coal. However, they may well be prevented from co-operating in this way by the activities of the smaller oil companies which in general terms aim at maximizing their sales in order to secure some return on the capital they have invested in producing and/or refining facilities and would not, therefore, voluntarily withdraw from the business. Thus, as in the United States, where the oil industry was at first asked to curb its imports of oil and then forced to do so by legislation, it seems likely that voluntary restraint in Europe will be unworkable and that specific government action—or inter-governmental action through the European Economic Community—will be necessary if the coal industry is to gain a respite from the competition from oil.

Throughout much of Europe, therefore, the prospects for government directed or influenced energy policies, which will help to determine the rate at which the demand for oil will increase, seem fairly certain. As a result, the rapid rise in oil consumption in the 1950s (an average of 12·7 per cent. per annum with an even faster rise in the last three years of the decade), is likely to be contained to some degree in the 1960s. From this kind of approach, however, one would expect the Scandinavian countries and Italy to be excluded as they are dependent on imported fuels to a very large degree. In these countries the main consideration would appear to be continued efforts to minimize the unit cost of imported energy. These markets will thus represent important outlets for the supplies of cheap crude and products that will continue to be available, and this should ensure in these countries a rapidly rising consumption of oil. The division between the indigenous energy producers on the one hand and the energy importing countries on the other may be a stumbling block in the moves towards economic integration in Europe. The coal-producing members of the E.E.C. might reasonably anticipate openings for their surplus production in other parts of the Community— certainly in preference to coal imported from outside the area and possibly in preference to imported oil. Italy, and any other countries in a similar position which decide to join the Common Market, can be expected to resist such pressure and insist on having access to the cheapest supplies of energy that are available.*

* Common Market energy policy was still being negotiated at the time of writing.

Thus, politico-economic decisions that will have to be taken both by individual European governments and by European organizations will obviously affect the future pattern of oil demand in the region. The overall effect of these developments, coupled with the less rapid rate of economic growth in the future than in the immediate past and the generally more efficient use of fuel, seems on balance likely to reverse the process in which, over the last decade, Western Europe has steadily increased its share of oil consumption in the world outside North America and the Soviet bloc. From 1950 to 1960 Western Europe's consumption rose from 36 to 53 per cent. of the total. In the next decade its share may well fall back to under 50 per cent., as demand in the developing countries increases more quickly than in Europe.

Japan

As shown in Chapter 4, few parts of the world outside North America and Western Europe have achieved a high *per capita* consumption of oil. Japan is the most significant exception, but even this is a relatively recent development, reflecting the rapid growth of the Japanese economy since 1950 and the success of oil in expanding its markets at the expense of coal.

In 1950 the Japanese economy was essentially based on coal, which provided about 83 per cent. of the total commercial energy consumption of some 44 million tons of coal equivalent. Oil provided less than 5 per cent. of the total. By 1960 energy consumption had more than doubled but the percentage provided by coal had slumped to about 46 per cent. Oil's share of the total had increased to almost 35 per cent., with a rise in consumption over the decade from about 3 million tons to almost 25 million tons. The predominance of coal—supplied by generally high-cost domestic mines and by imports over distances of many thousands of miles from the United States and Australia—has thus been effectively challenged and for the next decade, when the consumption of energy seems likely to double again under the impact of further industrial expansion and a break-through into the mass market for motor vehicles, it is anticipated that oil will become the single most important source of energy.

The Japanese government's removal of currency controls—controls which have had the effect of limiting imports of oil in order to conserve supplies of foreign exchange—must lead to an enhanced rate of change from coal to oil. The fact that many of the leading Japanese steel companies also have connections with oil-importing concerns seems to suggest that the steel industry will be quick to take advantage of technological developments which permit the replacement of coking coal by oil, particularly as much of the coking coal itself has to be imported and cannot be obtained as cheaply as oil.

The Japanese market, then, may be expected to be highly attractive to companies with oil to spare, and the Soviet Union explicitly intends to make Japan one of the main outlets for its oil, in exchange for capital and other goods to assist in the industrialization of the Soviet Far East. This development will be facilitated with the completion of the Trans-Siberian pipeline, which will significantly reduce the cost to the Soviet Union of supplying the Japanese market and thus enable it to offer even more competitive terms.

In many ways, changes in oil demand in Japan resemble those in Western Europe, but with the significant difference that in Japan there is not the same high degree of concern for the protection of the indigenous coal industry. The high-cost coal industry with a current production of about 50 million tons and employing 150,000 workers, does not hold the same significant place in the economy as, for example, does the United Kingdom coal industry which, in a country with little more than 50 per cent. of Japan's population, employs over 560,000 people and has a production of almost 200 million tons per annum. Thus the impact of government action designed to protect domestic coal against imported oil is unlikely to be as important a factor in slowing down the increase in the demand for oil in Japan as it is in Western Europe.

The Developing Countries

Throughout most of the rest of the world—except for Australia, New Zealand, some of the small Persian Gulf States where there is a large use of oil fuel in the refineries, and in the Soviet Union and the countries of Eastern Europe where the factors accounting for the use of oil have already been briefly examined (see pages 49–52)—the *per capita* consumption of oil products remains low, although, as noted in Chapter 4, it is increasing rapidly. In general terms this reflects the world pattern of under-development with its features of low incomes per head, little personal ownership of oil-using equipment and with only a minority of the population engaged in energy consuming industrial and associated activities. In these areas it is even more difficult to establish a correlation between economic development and energy use, for the opening of one energy intensive plant, such as an iron and steel plant or a cement factory, may have a tremendous impact on energy consumption with a much smaller impact on the total national product. For example, total energy consumption in the Central American Republic of Costa Rica is about 250,000 tons of coal equivalent per annum. There have recently been proposals to exploit some large reserves of iron ore for smelting on the Pacific Coast before exporting it to the iron and steel industries of the United States, Japan and Europe. The establishment of this industry would lead to an additional use of energy for extracting the ore, transporting it to the coast for smelting, and for ancillary activities of about 2 million tons of coal equivalent per year. Thus, energy use in the country would be increased more than eight times whilst the development would increase the gross national product by no more than 20 per cent. Even in as large a country as Argentina, which has already undergone a quite lengthy period of industrial development, it has been estimated that the rate of increase in the demand for energy will be half as great again as the rate of development of the economy over the next decade.

Two general points should be noted before we go on to examine the situation in some of the countries in this group. The process of development in all these countries is to a very large degree based on industrialization, with a concurrent improvement in transport facilities. Secondly, in these countries so-called non-commercial forms of energy are still of importance. These include the use of wood, of vegetable waste (*e.g.* bagasse from the sugar industry), of dung and of any other combustible material which is readily available to a population which, although having small requirements, cannot afford to buy either energy in a more convenient form or the equipment in which to use it. With economic development implying a rise in the money incomes of some sectors of the population and their regular employment in factory, mine and workshop, which precludes the collection of wood, etc., there is a process of the substitution of non-commercial energy by products which have to be bought (*e.g.* kerosene for lighting and cooking). These two developments obviously lead to the need for rapidly expanding supplies of energy, and this, with particular reference to oil, often creates problems of financing the imports of the increasing quantities required and a consequent demand for the development of indigenous resources— a process which we have examined already (see Chapter 3) for its significance on the world pattern of oil production.

Latin America

In Latin America the relatively higher figures of *per capita* consumption of petroleum arise in part from the dominating position held by petroleum products in the supply of energy throughout the region, and in part from the greater degree of economic development than in most parts of Africa and Asia. In every country except Venezuela, where in 1960 natural gas became the single most important fuel, petroleum products provide the main source of commercial energy. The development of the overall position in the last thirty years is shown on Table 7 which indicates an eightfold increase in oil consumption during this period, when, moreover, the contribution of oil to the total energy supply increased from 54 to 76 per cent.

TABLE 7

LATIN AMERICA
Commercial Energy Consumption 1930–60

(in millions of metric tons of coal equivalent)

Year	Solid Fuels	Petroleum	Natural Gas	Hydro-electricity	Total
1930	9·7	12·0	0·3	0·3	22·3
1940	8·4	21·3	0·7	0·8	31·2
1950	8·8	46·5	4·5	1·9	61·7
1960	11·5	93·9	13·7	4·9	124·0

Sources: U.N. Statistical Papers, Series J and Shell International Petroleum Co. Ltd.

The four most significant petroleum consuming countries are Argentina, Brazil, Venezuela, and Mexico. In each of these countries there is little effective competition from solid fuel as local supplies are generally limited and of poor quality and imports are unable to compete with either indigenous or imported oil. The development of an iron and steel industry in each country * could provide an additional outlet for coal but it seems likely that the new methods of iron production, discussed on page 80, which greatly reduce the quantities of coke required in the blast furnace, will be introduced to avoid this possibility. In fact, a plant with a daily output of 500 tons of iron, using a direct reduction process based on natural gas, has recently been commissioned at Monterrey in Mexico.

It is somewhat paradoxical that in both Venezuela and Argentina, the former with a much greater oil production potential than the current annual output of about 150 million tons suggests and the latter with a rapidly rising production of oil, the demand for oil is now being contained by a rapidly rising consumption of natural gas. Of the total consumption of 10,275 million cubic metres of natural gas in Latin America, 85 per cent. is used in these two countries. In Venezuela, where about half of the natural gas produced is still 'flared off' (*i.e.* burnt to no useful purpose at the point of production), increasing use is being made of the large supplies available for refinery fuel—where it replaces fuel oil or other petroleum products— and there are plans for its greater use as a domestic and industrial fuel. In Argentina the construction of new pipelines from both the Campo Durán and the Comodoro Rivadavia fields to Buenos Aires has enabled the consumption of gas to increase very rapidly and additional pipeline capacity is under construction. Thus, although natural gas provided only 4 per cent. of Argentina's energy supplies in 1960, its share is expected to rise to over 20 per cent. by 1970. Elsewhere in Latin America natural gas does not seem likely to be an important contender for petroleum markets, although supplies may eventually be piped from Argentina to Chile and Uruguay to provide a new source of energy in both countries.

---

* In 1959 the Economic Commission for Latin America estimated that by 1975 a production of over 30 million tons of steel will be possible in Latin America compared with less than 5 million tons in 1960.

The situation elsewhere in Latin America may be illustrated by particular reference to Chile and Colombia. In Chile in the period 1950–60 the annual average growth in gross national product, in real terms, was about 2·5 per cent. Over the same period consumption of total energy, fluctuations in which show a fairly close correlation (of over 0·9) with those of gross national product, has increased at the somewhat higher rate of 3·1 per cent. per annum. Table 8 illustrates the changing pattern of energy use during this period.

TABLE 8

CHILE

Commercial Energy Consumption 1950 and 1960

(millions of metric tons of coal equivalent)

	1950		1960	
Total	4·9	*Percentage*	7·5	*Percentage*
Coal	1·7	35·7	2·1	27·8
Oil	2·1	43·1	3·5	47·0
* Hydro-electricity	1·0	21·2	1·8	28·2

Source: Shell International Petroleum Co. Ltd.

The table brings out the growing dominance of oil. This has arisen from a variety of factors, including the falling away of coal production in Chile from a peak of 2·55 million tons in 1952 to only 2 million tons in 1960 (the same level of production as in 1946); the shortage of capital in the country, which has prevented the utilization of hydro-electricity potential estimated at some forty times the present installed capacity; the rise in domestic oil production from 80,000 tons in 1950 to almost 1 million tons in 1960; and the ability of the major international oil companies established in Chile to bring in their increasing requirements from their producing areas in Venezuela and Colombia.

Because of the need to improve living standards for the mass of the population in Chile, the government has adopted a ten-year development programme [19] aimed at giving an annual increase in real gross national product of about 5·5 per cent.—

* Calculated on the basis of the amount of coal which would have been needed to generate this amount of electricity in a thermal station of average local efficiency.

more than twice the rate of growth for the past ten years. Such a plan, with its emphasis on the expansion of mining, industry and transport, will obviously call for a greatly increased consumption of energy. In fact, if the programme is carried through, the demand for energy could almost double to over 13 million tons of coal equivalent. Although the plan indicates that the hydro-electricity capacity is to be increased by about two-thirds and that there are also to be attempts to revive the declining coal industry (by government aid to coal mining companies adopting modernization programmes and by fiscal incentives to consumers using coal instead of oil) to bring production up to 2·8 million tons in 1970, the greater part of the increased demand for energy will fall on petroleum, whose use may increase from under 2·5 million tons to about 4·6 million tons by the end of the period—or even higher if the plans for the coal industry do not materialize or if the coal cannot be produced competitively even after modernization.

The Development Plan envisages Chilean production of oil rising from its present level of 1 million tons to over 3·5 million tons by 1970, but this is considered somewhat optimistic unless new fields are discovered in the north of the country to supplement the output from the Tierra del Fuego fields. The heavy cost of financing such exploration and development—operations which are presently restricted to the state enterprise, E.N.A.P. —would seem likely to place too great a burden on the country's finances, particularly on the need to find foreign exchange for importing the necessary capital equipment. However, the necessity to secure an additional 7 per cent. of oil supplies each year if the development programme is not going to run into a bottle-neck caused by energy shortages, and the equally great difficulty in finding the increasing amounts of scarce foreign exchange needed to finance its purchase from abroad, might lead to government grants of exploration concessions to foreign companies, which would, of course, provide their own equipment and supplies for the operation. It could well be a political development of this kind which would enable the *per capita* consumption of oil in Chile to increase from its present very modest level of 80 gallons to about 150 gallons by 1970.

The growth in the consumption of petroleum products in the upper Cauca valley of Colombia illustrates the types of changes that are likely to take place in an economically developing area. This part of Colombia has developed quite rapidly in the last ten years as a result of the expansion of both agriculture and industry. Agricultural growth has been based on an increase in the area of cultivated land (from about 1000 square miles in 1952 to 1400 square miles in 1958) and in the more intensive production of crops such as cotton and sugar. Manufacturing industry has become increasingly important. In the Department of Valle—covering the most important central part of the area—output from industry increased at an average rate of 11·4 per cent. per annum. Expansion in the economy is expected to continue.

The process of development has been reflected in the consumption of petroleum products. Between 1950 and 1960 consumption increased threefold to almost half-a-million tons. This rapid overall increase in the use of oil, however, masks the significant changes that have taken place at different times for different types of fuel as the needs of industry, agriculture, transport and the population have changed in the process of economic development and have reacted to the availabilities of alternative fuels.

For example, throughout the period the use of gasoline has steadily increased as the total number of vehicles expanded from 15,000 to over 40,000 to meet the rising demand for transport from the agriculture, industries and population of the area. This upward trend in gasoline consumption seems likely to continue and may be enhanced as irregularities in the supply of new vehicles (caused by the imposition of controls on the imports of vehicles because of periodical shortages of foreign exchange) are eliminated as a result of the gradual expansion of facilities to assemble cars and lorries in Colombia. The construction and improvement of roads in the valley seem likely to have the same effect.

Contrasting with the continued expansion of gasoline consumption is the falling rate of increase in the use of kerosene after a period of extremely rapid growth. This clearly illustrates the function of kerosene as an interim fuel in an area which is progressing through stages of economic development. Slightly improved living standards increased the demand for kerosene as an illuminating fuel, but the development of electricity production (83 per cent. hydro-electricity) and the establishment of a large-scale distribution network, which will eventually take electric power to the whole area, by the Cauca Valley Corporation (modelled on the Tennessee Valley Authority) will probably almost eliminate the use of kerosene for lighting purposes. Similarly, the rise in kerosene demand for cooking (both domestic and commercial) has resulted from changes in the way of living (*e.g.* increased industrialization) whereby kerosene was substituted for non-commercial fuels (notably wood). Kerosene will later be replaced by electricity or perhaps by liquified petroleum gases (propane and butane) as these fuels become available and as more people can afford the higher cost of the capital equipment necessary to use these fuels.

Industrial expansion—and its associated transport requirements—has its main impact on the use of the heavier petroleum products—diesel oil and fuel oil. The consumption of diesel fuel expanded fourfold in the 1950s with increasing use in industry, in shipping and on the railways, where it has, in part, replaced coal and fuel oil (as diesel locomotives replace steam engines). While these outlets are likely to be growing markets, the development of the area's hydro-electricity potential will, on the other hand, gradually eliminate the need for diesel-electricity generation and thus curb the expansion of demand for the fuel to some extent. By way of contrast, development in the market for fuel oil seems to lie ahead. Perhaps rather surprisingly, the consumption of this product in 1960 was not much greater than in 1950. The explanation lies in the local availability of coal on which industry in the Cauca Valley has traditionally been dependent. A significant price differential between coal and fuel oil—estimated in 1960 to be of the order of 75 per cent. on a calorie for calorie basis—has discouraged conversions from the former to the latter. However, it now seems possible that difficulties in expanding the output of coal (about 300,000 tons in 1960) without accompanying rises in costs and prices may enable fuel oil to compete more effectively, particularly if a refinery is constructed to serve the region and thus lead to lower prices for products which at the moment are mainly transported along the coast and through the Panama Canal from refineries on the Caribbean coast of Colombia. Moreover, the total market for coal or fuel oil in industry may expand much more quickly than in the last decade if plans to use bagasse (the residue after sugar has been extracted from the cane) for paper making, instead of continuing to use it as a fuel in the sugar mills, materialize.

Changes in the pattern of consumption in the Cauca Valley thus depend in part on the changing availability of competing fuels. In turn, of course, the changing pattern of consumption will affect the development of the energy supply industries. One can envisage the continued development of the hydro-electricity potential; difficulties for the coal mining industry as it attempts to reduce costs by rationalization in order to face competition from oil; and the construction of an oil refinery for the region as overall demand expands and as the demand for individual products more nearly approaches the product out-turn that can be obtained from the straight distillation of a readily available crude.

South-East Asia

Some of the world's lowest figures for *per capita* use of petroleum products are found in non-communist Asia (excluding Japan and Hong Kong). This is, for example, true of India, which accounts for about two-thirds of all the commercial energy consumed in this region of the world. This is in part a reflection of the low standards of well-being and in part a result of the high degree to which India is dependent on coal, which provides over 90 per cent. of the total supply of primary commercial energy. The demand for oil is thus effectively contained and seems likely to remain so for the next decade, as India cannot afford to replace readily available supplies of indigenous coal by imports of oil, which would quickly drain the country's limited foreign exchange resources. Foreign exchange problems thus provide a valid basis for a national energy policy and the denial of freedom of choice between fuels to potential consumers of oil instead of coal. Even so, the consumption of oil in the 1960s may be expected to double from its present level of about 5·5 million tons and oil will increase slightly its share of the total energy market. This,

H

however, will largely arise from the expansion of the non-competitive markets—particularly from the development of road transport, which is needed to overcome the bottle-neck in the economy caused by the overloading of the limited railway facilities in the country—and possibly from some degree of conversion from coal to oil when this can lead to a great improvement in the effective use of energy (*e.g.* on diesel locomotion on the railways). Some at least of the increased consumption of oil will, it is hoped, be met from indigenous resources, which are being developed as part of the third five-year plan.

In the rest of South-East Asia oil is the dominant source of commercial energy and is expected to continue to increase its share of the rapidly expanding energy market to the point where by 1970 it will provide about two-thirds of total requirements. Unlike Latin America, South-East Asia has a relatively unimportant hydro-electricity potential and, in any case, the necessary capital may not be available for projects which are possible. Neither is natural gas likely to assume a significant role, as it does in Argentina and Venezuela, with the possible exception of developments in Pakistan, where to date the search for oil has produced little oil but has indicated large potential gas supplies.

The precise pattern of developing oil demand depends, as we saw in the examination of the changing situation in the Cauca Valley in Columbia, on local conditions both of supply and of the changing needs of the economy.

This may also be illustrated by reference to the situation in South Vietnam, where during the period 1956–59, there was an abnormally high rate of growth in energy consumption as a result of rehabilitation measures and the release of a pent-up demand following the end of the war in the country. The oil industry was in the most favourable position to meet the expanding energy needs of the economy and by 1959 it was supplying about 95 per cent. of the total commercial energy used compared with under 90 per cent. three years earlier. The increasing imports of oil were, however, putting a strain on an already difficult foreign exchange situation and the government not only expressed its intention of holding further increases in energy consumption to the minimum consistent with the further development of industry, but also embarked on two major projects—the development of coal production at Nong Son and the construction of a large hydro-electricity station at Da Nhim—designed to boost domestic sources of energy and thus to save foreign exchange. Thus, although oil consumption will continue to increase in some sectors of the economy (for example, in diesel-electricity generation in rural areas and from increasing numbers of motor vehicles), the impact of the new sources of energy in industry and in the urban electricity supply may be sufficiently great temporarily to reduce the demand for fuel oil and thus may curb oil's overall contribution to total energy supply.

Thus, in all parts of the world—from a country such as the United States with an annual oil consumption per head of over 600 gallons a year right through to a country such as Vietnam with a *per capita* consumption of only about 12 gallons—the pattern of oil consumption and the significant changes in that pattern have to be examined in terms of the economy's need for energy and the ability of oil to compete successfully in supplying it. Furthermore, the success or otherwise of oil does not depend solely—or sometimes even mainly—on the price at which it is or could be laid down at the point of consumption in comparison with other fuels. It depends also—and probably increasingly in most parts of the world—on the political attitude adopted towards the various fuels that are physically available. This is particularly important where there are indigenous resources of energy which are protected, in order to avoid the problems associated with the rehabilitation of areas of a country dependent upon the continued production of its energy resource, or where there are resources which are utilized to their greatest possible extent either for security of supply reasons or because a country cannot afford the foreign exchange expenditure on imported products even if these are cheaper than the home-produced alternative.

A geographical interpretation of the pattern of demand for oil depends on a consideration of these and many other relevant factors—physical, social, political and economic. This chapter has provided an opportunity to pick out only some of the main strands in the present world pattern and to indicate some of the more likely developments in a rapidly changing situation in a few countries with problems that are both unique, in the context of the particular circumstances of the country concerned, and yet also typical of the complex situation concerning energy demand which exists in almost every country of the world.

REFERENCES

1 N. S. Ginsburg (Ed.) *Essays on Geography and Economic Development*, 1960. See Chapter V, *Energy Consumption and Economic Development* by N. B. Guyol for examples of studies which have been made.

2 See *United Nations Statistical Papers*, Series J, No. 5, p. 6 for a statement on the considerations involved in converting all forms of energy to a common unit.

3 *United Nations Statistical Papers*, Series E, No. 4. 'Per Capita National Product of 55 Countries, 1952–54', pp. 3–6.

4 Shell International Petroleum Co. Ltd., 'Oil; the next Ten Years.' *Oil and Gas Journal*, 28th December, 1959.

5 *Ibid.*

6 Central Electricity Generating Board: *Annual Report and Accounts, 1960–61*, pp. 25 and 167.

7 The following conversions to coal equivalent have been used:
   0·67 metric tons of oil products ⎫
   750 cubic metres of natural gas ⎬each equal 1 metric ton of coal.
   8000 kWh of hydro-electricity ⎭

8 United Nations *Monthly Bulletin of Statistics*, May 1962.

9 Shell International Petroleum Co. Ltd., *op. cit.*

10 *Hansard*. House of Commons. 8th November 1961. Col. 980.

11 From an address by Mr. P. E. Rousseau, Chairman of SASOL, to the 7th Commonwealth Mining and Metallurgical Congress, June 1961. Reported in *Petroleum Press Service*, July 1961, p. 268. See also *P.P.S.* January 1961, p. 25.

12 International Bank for Reconstruction and Development. *The Economic Development of Venezuela*, 1961, p. 222.

13 W. J. Levy *Oil and Gas in the B.T.U. Battle.* Report prepared for the Pontiac Refining Corp., 1959, p. 7.

14 *Petroleum Press Service.* 'Growing Markets for Gas', August 1960, p. 281. For a detailed consideration of the pricing policies of the natural gas industry see E. Neuner, *The Natural Gas Industry: Monopoly and Competition in Field Markets*, 1960.

15 See M. G. de Chazeau and A. E. Kahn *Integration and Competition in the Petroleum Industry* (Petroleum Monograph Series, Vol. 3, 1959), Chapter 9 for a detailed analysis of United States oil imports up to 1957 when they accounted for 13 per cent. of total oil consumed. (The United States became a net importer of crude and products in 1948.) In 1958, however, imports jumped to 19 per cent. of total

consumption and have since risen to over 21 per cent. in spite of import controls. The greatly increased flow of oil to the United States since 1957 seems to have been largely the result of the factors which led to an increased supply of oil outside the United States (see Chapter 3) and to low tanker freight rates across the Atlantic. De Chazeau and Kahn (pp. 205–211) anticipated this development but not the speed and intensity with which it came about.

16   D. L. Munby. 'Investing in Coal.' *Oxford Economic Papers* (New Series). Vol. 11, No. 3, October 1959, p. 250.

17   The Baade-Friendensburg report on Germany's supply of energy. Summarized in *Petroleum Press Service*, June 1962, p. 203.

18   W. J. Levy. 'Report on Coal-Oil Competition in Germany', 1961. Summarized in *Petroleum Press Service*, October 1961, p. 363.

19   *Programa Nacional de Desarrollo Economico 1961–70*. January 1961. This was formulated by the Corporación de Fomento de la Producción (CORFO), the official economic planning authority.

PART III

REFINING, TRANSPORT
AND
DISTRIBUTION

CHAPTER 6

The Pattern of Refining and the Determinants of Refinery Location

At the beginning of 1962 there were refineries on stream in seventy countries and there were projects under construction, or at the definitive planning stage in another twenty-four countries. Six years earlier in 1956 refineries were operating in only fifty-seven countries,[1] and in 1950 in only forty-one countries, about the same number as in 1939. The rapid proliferation of countries with refinery capacity has arisen as a result of the changing relative importance of the several factors that help to determine the places at which an oil company locates its manufacturing processes and any consideration of the pattern of refining is an integral part of the larger study of these factors.

Prior to the Second World War, oil refining was, to a very large degree, located in the major oil-producing areas of the world. At that time, in fact, over two-thirds of the world's refinery capacity was located in the United States which, as already shown (see page 17) was then responsible for almost two-thirds of the total world oil production. Since then the United States' share of oil production has fallen away to under one-third of the world total. During this period there has also been a fall—though to a lesser degree—in that country's share of world refinery capacity and it now stands at about 45 per cent. of the world total. The fact that the United States has retained a greater proportion of total world oil refining capacity than of world oil production reflects the growing importance of the refining industry's market location, for additional refining facilities have been established to process the increasing quantities of crude oil that the United States has had to import principally into areas remote from the main domestic resources. The changing relationship between production, refining and consumption in the United States is shown in Table 9.

In the rest of what is now the non-communist world (but excluding Canada), oil refining in 1939 was largely confined to countries which produced and exported oil. Thus of a total capacity of 85 million tons, almost 60 million tons was accounted for by refineries in Iran, Iraq, Bahrain, the Dutch East Indies and Borneo, Venezuela and the Netherlands West Indies, Colombia, Trinidad, Mexico, Peru and Ecuador. By

TABLE 9

THE UNITED STATES IN THE WORLD OIL INDUSTRY

	U.S. Oil Production (mills. m. tons)	Percentage of World Total	U.S. Consumption (mills. m. tons)	Percentage of World Total	U.S. Refining Capacity (mills. m. tons)	Percentage of World Total
1939	170	63	165	60	225	71
1950	270	51	322	61	335	64
1960	345	33	485	44	498	46

Source: Oil Trade Journals

1939, the Abadan refinery was being supplied with crude from all the Iranian oilfields and was capable of turning out some 10 million tons of products per annum. The then recently constructed refinery on the island of Bahrain had a capacity of 1·6 million tons and was processing oil from the Awali field. Venezuelan oil at this date was being refined mainly in the off-shore islands of Aruba and Curaçao which form part of the Netherlands West Indies, but there was also some capacity in Venezuela itself. The refineries at Pointe à Pierre and Point Fortin in Trinidad were designed to process the rising production of local crude and, in the case of the latter refinery, to provide additional facilities for crude from nearby Venezuela. Of the remaining refineries around the world, with a total capacity of only some 25 million tons per annum, not all were located in consuming areas for they included, for example, the refinery at Haifa (with a capacity of 1 million tons), located on the eastern seaboard of the Mediterranean, to which pipelines from the oilfields of north-east Iraq delivered the supplies of crude oil. The location of this refinery was, of course, related to that of the producing area. There was a transport advantage to be gained from moving the crude to a coastally located refinery when compared with the alternative of refining on the oilfields and then moving the products to the coast.

In the consuming areas, the refineries of France, the United Kingdom and Japan were the most important but it should be borne in mind that even so the refinery capacity in these three countries was only 7·6, 3·8 and 2·6 million tons respectively. By the outbreak of war in 1939, however, it is possible to discern a move of refining towards the growing consuming areas of Europe, for in the previous few years new capacity had been established in Italy, Germany, Belgium and Holland. At this period the sales of individual companies were developing to a volume at which local refining by these companies was becoming a more attractive proposition. Shell-Mex and B.P. Ltd. in the United Kingdom, for example, sold about 5 million tons of oil products in 1938 and in Germany, Shell's sales approached 1·5 million tons.

The development of new trends in the pattern of refining was naturally curbed by wartime conditions. During the war it became necessary to make use of whatever facilities existed to provide for the essential needs of the armed forces and of industry and commerce. The major consideration in the supply and refining of petroleum was the need of the war effort. Thus, United States capacity, together with that of the Venezuelan/Caribbean export complex, was used—and expanded as necessary—to meet the demands of the Atlantic and western hemisphere areas. Abadan and the Egyptian and Palestine refineries were expanded to provide oil products for the remainder of the allied world. As a result of wartime exigences the Abadan refinery had its capacity nearly doubled to an annual figure of 17 million tons.

Two main locational trends can be distinguished in the post-war refining industry outside the United States. The earlier, and still the more significant, development has been the continuation and massive strengthening of the trend that has already been noted for the immediate pre-war years—the growth of refining capacity in the major consuming areas of Europe and Japan. The cause of this development has generally been defined as the predominance of the pull of the market over the pull of the raw material.[3] It is difficult, however, to see the justification for simply looking at the change in terms of locational theory which, in its efforts to show that location in a market economy will be made at places where production plus transport costs are at a minimum, implies that in the competitive process the less effectively located units will be driven out of existence by the more effectively located ones. In fact, the nature of the vertically integrated international petroleum industry, whereby the same integrated company (or group of associated companies) owns not only producing facilities but also refining facilities in both the producing and the consuming areas and the means of transporting both crude and products between the two areas, would seem to eliminate the possibility of analyzing location on the basis of these theoretical considerations. The relationships between 'production costs' and 'transport costs' become a matter of merely juggling figures internal to the company concerned which will be under pressure (for tax and other reasons) to distribute its profit-earning capacity in part according to criteria other than strictly economic ones. Thus, an associated refining company of one of the eight international groups located in a major consuming area does not buy its intake of crude from the cheapest source or sell its out-turn of products to the highest bidder. It merely handles and processes crude as directed by the central offices of the international company. In such a situation—an extremely common one in view of the ownership of about 71 per cent. of refining capacity outside North America and the Soviet bloc by the major international companies—it would appear not to be particularly useful to examine refinery location in terms of the economics of the free market economy.

The international firms, however, are concerned with minimizing the overall cost of the several processes involved in getting the oil out of the ground and through to the consumer. Economies at intermediate stages are, therefore, considered important, and, as will be shown later, the greater reductions effected in the costs of shipping crude compared with smaller economies in the costs of moving products have been one of the means by which savings could be achieved, and this has had an impact on the location of refineries near to certain markets. Such considerations have not necessarily, or even mainly, been the deciding factors in determining the location of refining. Decisions concerning location have also had to take into account several other important factors.

The first is the physical problem whereby a company working internationally has to match, as closely as possible, both quantitative and qualitative demand from area to area with available supply. Successful penetration of a particular market perhaps remote from a convenient source of supply of refined products implies that consideration will be given to the desirability of building a refinery to feed this outlet although the need for such a development may often be postponed or even eliminated by means of an 'exchange' agreement with another company whereby a surplus in another area will be 'sold' to the competitor in exchange for supplies of an equivalent value in the area in question. Thus capital expenditure is saved to the advantage of both companies concerned. If such an exchange is impossible or undesirable, then the viability of the proposed refinery will be presented by comparing the cost of buying and delivering the products at the formally posted prices with the cost of manufacturing the products from an appropriate crude also delivered at the formally posted price.* The irrelevance of this exercise to the theoretical approach to locational theory arises from the artificiality of the posted price system, which is now little more than the basis on which decisions concerning royalty payments are made and on which transfers between associated companies of the same group are normally based.

A second factor is the political pressures on the oil industry, pressures to which more attention will be given later. These may, for example, virtually compel a company to build a refinery in a given country if it is to be allowed to remain in business by the government. In such a case economic factors become unimportant in decisions concerning refinery location.

A third factor is the strategy of the oil company. (Strategic

---

* This exercise will not, however, alone form the basis on which a decision whether or not to build the refinery will be taken. It will also depend on the other factors examined later in this chapter.

considerations of a national character may be counted as one of the political factors noted in the previous paragraph.) From the oil company's point of view, 'refining eggs' are perhaps better kept in a separate basket from 'producing eggs' so as to ensure that in the event of international tension or of expropriation of facilities, the only worry is to replace crude supplies and thus to eliminate the additional worry of having to find an alternative place at which the oil can be refined.

With these several considerations in mind we may turn to examine the development of the refining industry in Western Europe. In 1939 the capacity of the industry was only 17 million tons; capacity at the beginning of 1962 was about 250 million tons working at a very high load factor, under-utilized capacity being restricted mainly to Italy and Western Germany. During this period, Western Europe's share of total refinery capacity outside North America and the Soviet bloc has increased from 20 to over 40 per cent. Figures 7 and 8 show the pattern of refinery development in Western Europe in the period since 1950. Three significant developments can be seen; firstly, the increasing numbers of refineries; secondly, their increasing size; and thirdly, their increasingly widespread distribution. One outstanding result that this development has achieved is to increase the percentage of total demand for petroleum products met from local refineries from only 25 per cent. in 1939 to more than 85 per cent. in 1962, and this in spite of a six-fold increase in total consumption. Several factors have combined to produce this result.

The post-war trend in the Western European consumption of petroleum products has led to an increase in the proportion of fuel oil in the total supplies required. The pattern of supplies required thus began to match more closely the most economical pattern of refining the commoner crudes. European refineries became much more likely to be able to find local outlets for all their products. The earlier need to back-haul the fuel oil not required in Europe has thus been eliminated.

The increased demand for all products in all European countries has produced a situation in which adequately sized refineries can be built. Thus refineries having a capacity of some 2–4 million tons a year, which produce quite significant economies of scale,[4] became feasible in most countries—even in small countries such as Norway, Denmark and Eire, where the overall demand for petroleum products in each case is of the order of 2 million tons. Although this total demand may be divided among several companies, arrangements are often made either for the construction of a jointly owned and operated refinery to supply all the country's needs or for the smaller distributors to draw their supplies from the refinery built by the market leader. Alternatively, because of the relatively small distances between countries in Europe and the general feasibility of shipping by sea, some companies have been able to build a refinery of this order of magnitude to serve the collective needs of its marketing affiliates in neighbouring countries.

Although it has been estimated that it is still somewhat cheaper to refine crude in much larger refineries (of a capacity of up to 7 million tons per annum), which can in general be built in producing rather than in consuming areas, the savings on the refining process are more than offset by the higher cost of shipment of products than of crude. Thus, a marketing company with annual sales of 2 million tons seems likely to achieve a net saving by having its refinery on the spot and importing its crude requirements rather than by buying and importing its products from a larger and somewhat lower cost refinery in a producing area.

This trend towards more economic refining in Europe has also been assisted by technical developments in the refinery industry. These developments have permitted a much greater degree of flexibility in refinery operations. The out-turn of products from a given crude can be varied and hence the output of the market oriented refinery can, within quite wide limits, be adjusted as necessary to match the demand of the market. This flexibility eliminates the need to find alternative export outlets for surplus products or to import other products to make up the local deficiences, as was the case when a refinery's out-turn of products was much more rigidly determined by the simple separation of the hydro-carbon components of a crude on the basis of the differences in their physical properties. The importance of this factor is seen in the way in which the

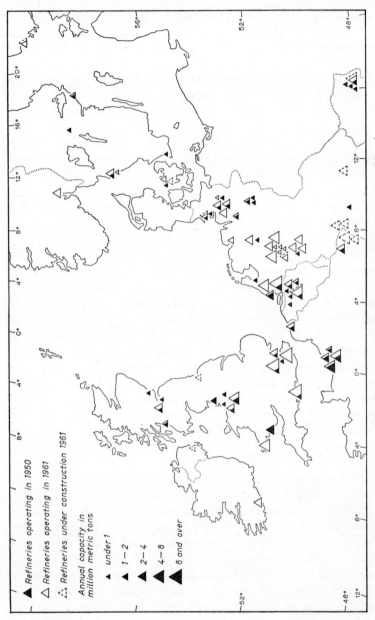

▲ Refineries operating in 1950
△ Refineries operating in 1961
⬩ Refineries under construction 1961

Annual capacity in
million metric tons

▴ under 1
▴ 1–2
◭ 2–4
◮ 4–8
◭ 8 and over

Figure 7. The Pattern of Refining in Western Europe—North

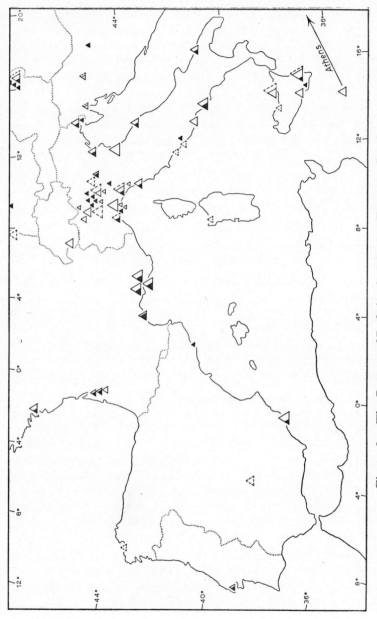

Figure 8. The Pattern of Refining in Western Europe—South

Western European refineries have gradually adjusted their output to match a more rapidly increasing demand for fuel oil and diesel oil than for the lighter products. Table 10 shows how the demand for main products has changed in some of the largest Western European countries between 1950 and 1960.

Government policies in most Western European countries have also attracted refinery capacity. Such policies have involved the use of both the 'carrot' and the 'stick'. The

TABLE 10

THE CHANGING DEMAND FOR MAIN PRODUCTS IN MAJOR WESTERN EUROPEAN COUNTRIES 1950–60

(Each product as percentage of total demand)

Country	Gasoline		Kerosene		Gas/Diesel Oil		Fuel Oil	
	1950	1960	1950	1960	1950	1960	1950	1960
United Kingdom	35·6	19·4	9·3	4·0	17·9	15·5	21·2	44·3
West Germany	29·8	20·0	7·2	n.a.	30·2	41·6	12·0	23·8
Italy	15·6	13·7	4·3	1·0	17·7	14·8	54·0	59·0
France	27·1	23·3	1·2	1·6	23·9	35·7	36·5	24·4
Sweden	16·8	12·8	5·0	2·0	30·1	33·6	41·5	44·5

Source: Oil Industry Trade Journals

parlous state of most of the countries' economies at the end of the war necessitated strict limitation on the amount of foreign currency that could be spent on importing oil. In particular, the shortage of dollars meant that a continuation of the practice of importing a very large percentage of Europe's needs for oil products from the United States and from other 'dollar' refineries in the western hemisphere could not be countenanced, and pressure was therefore exerted by governments for the expansion of refining in Europe. It has been estimated, for example, that from 1949 to 1955 a saving of foreign exchange of the order of £160 million was made as a result of the gradual change from product to crude oil imports into the O.E.E.C. countries of Western Europe.[5] Therefore, by making dollars available for importing American refining equipment, by permitting crude oil to enter duty free but charging significant duties on petroleum products, together with the political pressure that governments are generally in a position to bring to bear on oil companies, the development of refining capacity was given an important fillip.

Finally, both governments and oil companies have become increasingly concerned with the need for ensuring continuity of oil supplies in the face of various political uncertainties in the producing areas of the world.   The growing significance of oil to the economic health of Europe has been examined in Chapter 5 (see pages 86–92).   Before 1939, a shortage of oil would in general have been no more than an inconvenience for most West European countries.   A similar shortage today would cause severe dislocations in the economy as a result of the growth in importance of road transport, the use of oil in rail transport and the great development of diesel oil and fuel oil as industrial and commercial fuels.

It is, of course, partly the fear of the dislocation of overseas supplies of oil that provides the impetus to national energy policies (also discussed in Chapter 5) aimed at reducing the dependence of a country on imported fuels.   An alternative, or additional, way of reducing such dependence is to locate oil refineries at home.   With refineries located in Europe the only necessity, in the event of the disruption of supplies from an oil producing area, would be to find an alternative source of crude.   That would be difficult, but certainly not impossible: the success of oil exploration and development (see Chapters 1 and 2) has provided a large reserve of shut-in capacity which could be quickly utilized.   With refineries located at the sources of the crude, dislocation involves not only finding an alternative crude supply but also finding somewhere else to refine it.   This could in fact be a physical impossibility if the dislocation were large, as refinery capacity in general is not developed greatly in excess of estimated needs.

The nationalization in 1951 of the assets of the Anglo-Iranian oil company and the subsequent closure of the great Abadan refinery (processing Anglo-Iranian's output), whose output of some 25 million tons of products was providing the United Kingdom, for example, with about 20 per cent. of its petroleum requirements, effectively emphasized the dangers of dependence

on overseas supplies of refined products and stimulated a wave
of refinery development in Western Europe.   The wisdom of
the policy is seen in the fact that the existence of adequate
refinery capacity in Western Europe in 1956 greatly simplified
the problem of supplying the area with the required quantities
of oil at the time of the Suez crisis.   Had the refinery facilities
Europe needed still been located largely in the Arab countries,
some at least of them might have been closed down together
with the Suez Canal and some of the pipelines to the Mediterranean.   Even if they had remained in operation, the much
more complicated revised supply pattern necessitated by the
closure of the Canal might have proved too difficult to organize
quickly and effectively.   The validity of this is indicated by a
comment by P. H. Frankel, who suggests that even the re-
organization of crude supply routes proved almost too complex
an operation in the face of the many interests that were
involved.   In an article which analyzed the problems of oil
supplies attendant upon the Suez crisis he observed:

> 'The repercussions of the crisis were less dramatic than they
> were at one time expected to be.   This was due to the warm
> winter, the fact that demand was also for some other reason below
> estimate and to the skill with which all parties concerned handled
> their problems. . . . However, most people who are aware of
> the facts involved know how narrowly we escaped being faced
> with a very ugly situation.' [6]

Concern expressed by the governments of consuming
countries over the location of too much refinery capacity in
the producing areas has to some degree been shared by the
oil companies, which are anxious for the security of their
investments in parts of the world which have become much
less stable with the rise of nationalism.   This is particularly so
in the Middle East, where the pre-war influence and control
by Great Britain and France have so declined that investments
made by oil companies can no longer be guaranteed if necessary
by force of arms.   The failure to take any counteraction at
Abadan in 1951 and the debacle of Suez in 1956 illustrate this
point.   The recurrent political crises, often backed by threats
against the oil 'imperialists', have necessarily reduced the
confidence of the oil companies, which with enormous capital

assets tied up in producing and associated activities have naturally been hesitant to commit even more of their funds to the same areas for the development of refinery capacity. It is preferable to spread the risk by investing in refineries located in Europe where the possibilities of expropriation are somewhat more remote and where the refineries are always available to utilize crude from whatever part of the world is not affected by a political crisis.

An examination of the development of the refining industry in Japan indicates the influence of the same factors during the post-war period. Petroleum supplies were the responsibility of the United States military authorities for six years after the war and for most of this period Japan was supplied with imported products. In 1950, however, the country's need to save foreign exchange was recognized and permission was given for nine small refineries, with a total capacity of under 2 million tons, to be rehabilitated. Contemporary comment on the decision suggests that 'questions of comparative costs were outweighed by the need to save foreign exchange and by the desire to provide employment'.[7] It was estimated that these refineries would bring about a saving of over £3 million a year in the foreign exchange costs of Japan's petroleum imports. When military control of the oil industry ended in 1951, refinery construction boomed under the impact of a very rapidly rising demand for oil (see page 92) and government encouragement of the development. These factors have remained significant through to 1962 and the major international oil companies—as well as local Japanese interests— have been prepared to finance the growth of the industry so that, by bringing in crude rather than more expensive products, they could secure maximum supplies from their limited allocation of foreign exchange for overseas purchases of oil. By the beginning of 1962, the capacity of the Japanese refining industry had increased to over 50 million tons per year—only slightly less than the capacity in the United Kingdom—and at that time another 23 million tons of annual capacity were under construction or planned to be on stream before the end of 1964. The Japanese refinery industry will then be larger than that of any other country—except the United States and the Soviet Union.

Thus, for Western Europe and Japan political and strategic considerations, as well as the impact of national economic policies, have strongly reinforced the probable, though unquantifiable, economic advantages of locating refineries at the market rather than at the point of production.

The second main trend in the post-war location of the refining industry can be explained, however, principally in terms of political and economic nationalism. This aspect has been the building of refinery facilities in most other countries of the world. In this development the question of the comparative costs of making oil products available from refineries sited on the one hand at the source of the raw material and on the other in the area of demand has been but a minor consideration. Figures 9 and 10 show the location and size of the refineries in Latin America, South-East Asia and Africa, differentiating between those that were operating in 1950, those that came on stream in the 1950s and those that were either under construction or at the planning stage in 1961. Compared with 1950, when there were only ten countries in Latin America and four countries in South-East Asia with refining facilities, there are now only fourteen countries out of a total of forty-four in these two under-developed regions of the world without a refinery. It is only in Africa, where most of the countries have become independent within the last few years, that there is a significant number of states still without a refinery. This we may judge to be a merely temporary phenomenon, for the forces to be discussed below that have led to the extension of refining into Latin America and South-East Asia are equally at work in the newly independent nations of Africa.

Of the 118 existing or planned refineries in these three regions (except those producing mainly for export), only twenty-six exceed 2 million tons in annual capacity. Yet this size of refinery has been described by Frankel and Newton as the minimum at which a 'reasonably economic refinery can still be built'.[8] The remainder of the refineries are small ones with capacities ranging down to only 200,000 tons per year. They may be considered uneconomic in that they are manufacturing petroleum products which cost more to produce than the alternative supplies of products refined and shipped from the

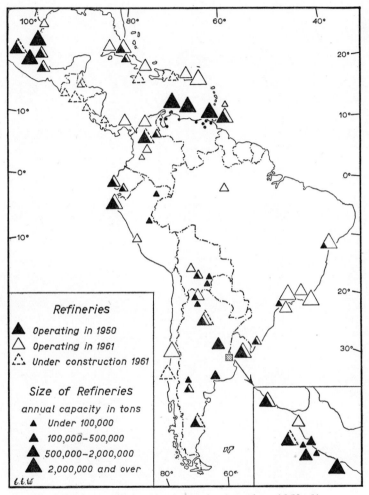

Figure 9. Refineries in Latin America, 1950–61
(See Figure 15 for the capacity of Venezuelan refineries)

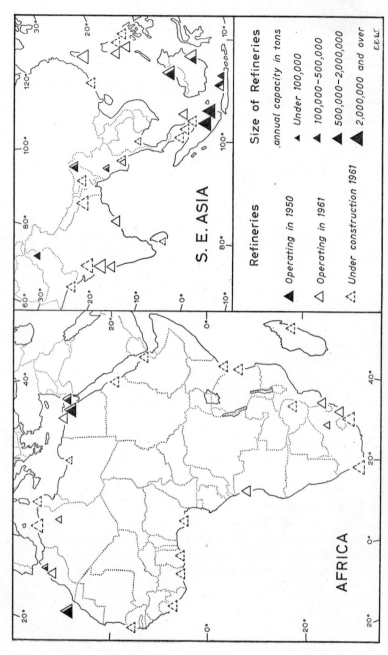

Size of Refineries

annual capacity in tons

▲ Under 100,000
▲ 100,000–500,000
▲ 500,000–2,000,000
▲ 2,000,000 and over

S. E. ASIA

Refineries

▲ Operating in 1950
△ Operating in 1961
△ Under construction 1961

AFRICA

Figure 10.   Refineries in Africa and South East Asia, 1950–61

nearest existing major refinery.* It has been estimated, for example, that one of these smaller refineries processing crude from Venezuela needs duty protection of the order of 90 United States cents per barrel (approximately £2. 8s. per ton) in order to make it competitive with products shipped at posted prices from one of the refineries in Venezuela or the Netherlands Antilles.[9]

The small size of most of these refineries arises quite simply from the fact that petroleum demand in most of the countries concerned is still relatively modest. In only ten countries (excluding Venezuela, Colombia and Indonesia, which are important producing countries and in which refineries have been located essentially to manufacture products for export) does the annual demand for all petroleum products exceed 2 million tons. Three of these countries, moreover—Argentina, Brazil and India—are too large for a single refinery to be able to cover the needs for all parts of the country. In Brazil, for example, from refineries located to serve the needs of the two major consuming areas of Rio de Janeiro and Sao Paulo, products for other parts of the country would have to be shipped distances of up to 2500 miles and those en route to the northern states would be well over half-way back to the Venezuelan export terminals from which the crude probably originated. Neither is it possible to meet the demand for products for the widely scattered main consuming areas of India—Bombay, Calcutta, Madras, etc.—from a refinery in one area without getting involved in the uneconomic transport of products. Thus, even in these large countries with an overall national demand large enough to sustain economic refineries, the dispersion of the effective demand for oil over widely-spaced areas of each country means that several smaller

---

* It should be pointed out, however, that faced with the inevitability of building refineries in these countries, great efforts have been made in the last few years to reduce manufacturing costs in small refineries by the development of new techniques such as the prefabrication of refinery units. The small refineries, moreover, are usually kept as simple as possible to limit the capital investment required. Such refineries, therefore, cannot handle a variety of crudes, their out-turn of main products is inflexible and they do not manufacture special products such as aviation gasoline, lubricating oils and bitumen. An oil company expert suggested that these developments have made economic refineries smaller than the minimum 2 million tons per annum suggested by Frankel and Newton. This may, however, only be a difference over what is meant by 'reasonably economic' and would not seem to invalidate the main thesis advanced in this section.

refineries have to be built in order to provide an effective supply of nationally refined products.

Thus, in general, one cannot explain the development of refineries in these three regions of the world as a move to the market to achieve economies in manufacturing and transport costs. As previously suggested, the main factor in the development is the impact of the forces of political and economic nationalism, although this has been reinforced by the influence of increasing competition among the growing number of international suppliers of crude oil. These suppliers have continually attempted to secure additional outlets for their oil— if necessary, by offering to build refineries even in the least promising locations.

The principal consideration has undoubtedly been the desire on the part of most countries to reduce the foreign exchange cost of importing energy. So far as this is true, the developing countries have merely been following the precedent set by the more developed countries for, as shown earlier in the chapter, many European countries adopted the policy of securing national refineries in order to make immediate savings of foreign exchange by importing crude oil rather than oil products. As most of the countries in Latin America and South-East Asia suffer from a permanent problem of balance of payments, the attraction of immediate savings in foreign exchange through the establishment of a refinery industry invariably outweigh any long-term arguments based on the fact that the cost of importing products is lower than the domestic cost of production.

In addition to this national economic pressure for refinery construction, a second, and less defensible, consideration has often been apparent. This is the belief that a refinery, like an airline and a shipping company, is a national status symbol which no self-respecting sovereign state can afford to be without. Thus oil refineries tend to acquire a political, as well as an economic, significance.

The means for securing these economic and political objectives fall into two main categories. In the first place, the state may reserve to itself the right to construct and operate a refinery (or refineries) designed to provide the country with the petroleum products it needs. This has been done in several Latin American countries—Chile, Uruguay and Brazil—where, with minor exceptions, the refining industry has been reserved to the state-owned and operated sector of the economy.   The important advantage of this type of development is that the crude requirements (except in as far as locally produced crude may have to be used) can be put out to tender and in a situation of a general world surplus of crude, which has existed since 1958 and which seems likely to continue into the forseeable future, supplies are obtainable at prices much below those 'posted' by the international companies.   Thus, in 1961, Brazil was able to obtain its crude imports at an average c.i.f. price of about $2.44 per barrel (about £6 per ton).   This probably represented an average saving of at least 35 cents per barrel on posted prices plus normal freight rates and thus a total saving in the year on the imports of 8 million tons of crude of more than £7 million.   Similar advantages seem likely to have accrued to Uruguay.   In 1961 tenders were invited for the supply to the state-owned refinery of crude oil for the next three years.   An indication of the state of the world market is given in the fact that no fewer than nine tenders were received.   No single company or organization secured the right to provide all the oil required, but Gulf Oil did secure a contract for about half the total requirement by offering to deliver Kuwait oil at a c.i.f. price of $2.05 per barrel.   With a 'posted' price of $1.59 per barrel for Kuwait oil and an 'assessed freight rate' from the Persian Gulf to the River Plate of $1.05 per barrel, Uruguay has obtained from Gulf a discount of about 20 per cent., representing a saving of more than 50 cents per barrel on the transaction.   With an annual requirement of over 1·5 million tons of oil, the ability of Uruguay to secure its supplies on such favourable terms gives an overall saving in foreign exchange of more than £2 million—over 3 per cent. of the country's total import bill.

Until recently the ability of most countries to seek political and economic objectives by financing and constructing their own refinery capacity has been limited by the difficulty, in general, of finding the necessary capital from over-stretched national budgets and, in particular, of obtaining the foreign exchange to buy the refinery equipment and to secure the technical know-how from overseas suppliers in the United States or Europe. The United States government was not until recently prepared to give grants or to make loans for refinery development on the grounds that private enterprise capital is always available for this purpose and that the socialistic practice of state refining should not be financed with American money.

A new factor has, however, served to alter this situation. The ability and willingness of the Soviet Union to finance oil producing operations (see Chapter 3) has paralleled a willingness and ability to provide loans and technical aid for the construction of state-owned refineries in the developing parts of the world. Thus, India's desire to build up the country's refinery capacity and to include this development in the state sector of the economy was made into a practical possibility by the offer of the Soviet Union to finance two refineries and by Rumania's willingness to build another one. Refineries financed by the Soviet Union (or by Rumania and Czechoslovakia, the other two countries of the Soviet bloc engaged in refinery engineering) have either been built or are planned in Egypt, Syria, Ethiopia and Cuba. Other offers were under consideration at the end of 1962.

The provision of refineries represents a readily obtainable objective for the Soviet Union and its allies, for the amount of aid involved is relatively limited (a 2 million tons per annum refinery can be built for a matter of £10–£15 million), and refinery equipment and 'know-how' are available for such purposes from a rapidly expanding domestic industry. In return for this limited investment, the Soviet Union seems to be assured of a favourable response from the countries in which the refineries are built, for they are a source of political pride and also a means whereby the control of the foreign oil companies—often regarded as the bastions of neo-colonialism in the former colonial areas—over the essential oil supplies can be finally broken.

The potency of reasoning of this type is seen perhaps in the somewhat surprising acceptance of Soviet help by Ethiopia whose government can certainly not be accused of dalliance with communism or even with neutralism. In Ethopia, however, there was much official dissatisfaction with the prices charged for oil products by the major international oil companies operating there. The government's inability to win the price concessions to which it considered the country was entitled must have been a major factor in persuading it to seek 'independence' by accepting a Soviet refinery.

The growing number of state-controlled refineries built with Soviet help could thus prove to be a major political and economic embarrassment not only for the international oil companies with their headquarters in the United States and Europe but also for the governments of these countries, which would be obliged to support the commercial interests of the companies in the event of conflict with the interests of the countries in which they are operating. Although something of a special case, it is perhaps significant that the major deterioration in United States–Cuban relationships occurred after Fidel Castro took over the refineries owned and operated by United States and British companies following their refusal to accept supplies of oil from the Soviet Union offered at a price some 20 per cent. below that which Cuba had had to pay for supplies from producing companies in Venezuela associated with the refinery operators.*

There is, however, an alternative to the construction of a state refinery. This involves the countries of Latin America, South-East Asia and Africa persuading the oil companies to finance and operate a refinery project. Although it might be supposed that very great persuasive power would be needed to achieve this, because the construction of a small refinery to provide the required products for a given country is uneconomic in the sense that these supplies could be made available at a lower overall cost from a large export refinery situated at the source of the crude, companies have in fact proved willing to spend money on building such refineries. Often in fact very little persuasion has been needed and sometimes competing companies have almost fallen over themselves to secure the 'privilege' of building an uneconomic refinery. Such perverse behaviour is understandable only when potentially excessive

---

* The companies argued that they had invested money in building the Cuban refineries to process their own and no one else's crude. Moreover, an attempt by the companies to meet Soviet prices would have produced a strong reaction in Venezuela where the government's income from oil is related to the prices actually realized on sales overseas.

supplies of crude oil are looking for a limited number of outlets and when these outlets sometimes fall under very effective government control. A company, having invested considerable sums of money in the search for and the discovery of oil, can secure no return on its investment until the oil is actually sold for refining. Thus many companies, notably the American 'independents', whose plight was noted in Chapter 3, without outlets for the crude they have so expensively discovered, have been tempted to offer to build refineries, knowing them to be uneconomic compared with larger refineries elsewhere, in order to obtain a secure outlet for at least part of their production and hence to obtain at least some return on the capital they have invested. The ability of such uneconomic refineries to compete with internationally traded products is secured either by heavy discounting of the crude supplies or, with the aid of the government concerned, by an appropriate degree of tariff protection or by quota controls on other imports or by the complete exclusion of any products which compete with those of the domestic refinery.

The major international companies have been obliged to play the refining game according to the new rules. Although they would prefer to utilize their refining capacity where the costs of doing so are at a minimum, their opportunities of continuing this practice are diminishing. The development for them is, moreover, far more serious than that which arises from any loss they might sustain on having to operate their large export refineries at less than capacity as new refineries are built in the consuming countries. The more serious aspect arises from the loss of an outlet for crude. If an independent refinery is built in a country in which the 'majors' are marketing products, then they will no longer be able to supply that market with their requirements from their overseas refineries—because of either tariff or quota regulations—but will instead have to purchase them from the independent competitor and thus use products made from some other company's crude. To avoid this loss of crude outlets, therefore, the 'majors' have been forced to build so-called defensive refineries. These may perhaps best be described as refineries which are in themselves uneconomic to operate but which when built ensure that the operating company can continue to supply the market with crude at prices which enable it to make an overall profit on its vertically integrated operations.

As a result of the interplay of these considerations bids for refineries have become increasingly competitive in recent years. Until the late 1950s an offer by one of the international companies to build a refinery was generally acceptable to the country concerned, which was also willing to grant the necessary degree of protection or quota controls in order to ensure that the refinery did not suffer from foreign competition. From the point of view of the company operating the refinery, an apparent profitability (essential to provide a basis for government taxation of the enterprise) could be achieved without undue increases in the prices of petroleum products by arranging for the crude to be supplied at a discount off the normal posted price. Moreover, the prices of petroleum products in these areas often reflected an absence of competition in the supply arrangements (as, for example, in the inter-company agreement on the supply of products to the French West African territories) and hence there was still a margin within which an uneconomic refinery could operate in supplying products at below the usual import prices.

However, the increasing competitiveness of bids for refineries has encouraged countries to stand out for more favourable conditions and offers. The major international companies have been forced to improve their terms to match those of companies trying to break into the market for the first time. In Ghana, for example, an offer by Mobil Oil to build a refinery was rejected in favour of an alternative proposal by the Italian company, E.N.I., which, in return for a monopoly right to process crude oil in sufficient quantities to meet the total all-company market demand and for certain tax concessions, offered the Ghanaian government a 50 per cent. share in the refinery without any payment whatsoever after it has been operating for ten years. Similarly, in Morocco and Tunisia refineries have been built by E.N.I. in which the state acquires a 50 per cent. interest. In Morocco the marketing companies have to take their product requirements from the refinery whereas they previously imported them from their own overseas sources.

Evidence of competition between one or more of the major

international companies anxious to preserve the outlets for themselves (and, by tacit agreement, for the other international companies as well) and E.N.I. is also seen in Tanganyika,where subsidiaries of several of the international companies have jointly offered to build a refinery.   E.N.I. has made alternative proposals which include provision for a government stake in the ownership of the facility and which seem likely to be successful.   In the Sudan, Shell and E.N.I. are contending for the right to build a refinery.   In Southern Rhodesia, the American independent, Aminoil, which produces crude in the Kuwait/Saudi Arabian Neutral Zone, offered to build a refinery which would have been large enough to meet the total needs of the Federation.   The main marketers, with the support of the other distributing companies, reacted with an alternative refinery proposal fearful of the loss of an outlet for products refined from their own crude.   Pressures on the government, and later from the government, brought about a compromise solution whereby a refinery is to be jointly con- structed by Shell/B.P. and Aminoil (which will have a 20 per cent. interest) and which will take the interests of the other marketing companies into account.

Thus, the international companies, which have in general tried to avoid having participation by local capital in their projects, as this severely limits their operating (*e.g.* pattern of supply) and financial flexibility, are now being forced, in the face of nationalist pressure and in the light of effective competi- tion from alternative suppliers and financiers, to reassess their attitude, and there has been some move towards local capital participation.   This is demonstrated in examples from four countries.   Two of the four refineries run by the major companies in the Phillipines are joint ventures with local capital participation ranging from 25 to 75 per cent. of the total investment.   A new refinery in Peru has been financed jointly by local capital and by the Californian Standard Oil Company.   In Thailand, the process of adaptation by the international companies has gone even further, as Shell have linked themselves with a local company, the Thai Oil Refinery Company, which is supported by French and Italian financiers, in order to secure the right to supply the crude to the refinery, which will, after ten years, revert to government ownership.

In Vietnam, in 1962, Shell and Esso agreed to build a refinery in which the government could take up 40 per cent. of the shares and local private capital another 10 per cent.

The overall impact of the increasingly diverse means of financing refineries in countries for which there can be no real justification on classical economic grounds must be to establish a pattern of refinery location which is more and more dispersed. It has already been suggested that most of the newly independent nations of Africa will follow the same course as that already adopted in the other developing continents. The justification for the process would seem to be even less in Africa, as the demand for oil is generally lower. Senegal, for example, has included plans for a 2 million tons refinery in its first five-year plan for economic development and will probably succeed in getting someone or other to build it or to finance it, even though the demand for oil in the country does not currently exceed half-a-million tons. The Liberian government has signed an agreement with a United States company for the construction of a 750,000 ton refinery. Liberian demand for petroleum products is of the order of 100,000 tons. Not only is a refinery of the agreed size uneconomic to operate but it also seems highly unlikely that it could work at more than a small fraction of its total capacity. The prospects for exporting the surplus products to other parts of West Africa must be remote as refinery proposals exist for most of the neighbouring countries, including Ghana, where the project is under construction, and Nigeria where local crude will provide the raw material.

The situation in Central America would seem to provide an excellent case-study in the development of refinery capacity in countries where the demand for petroleum products would not appear to justify its construction. Estimates of the demand for the principal petroleum products in Guatemala, Honduras, El Salvador, Nicaragua and Costa Rica in 1960 are set out in Table 11.

The table indicates that the total demand for all products throughout the area is less than 1·5 million tons per annum— a total demand less than sufficient to justify the construction of one economic refinery in the area, particularly in view of the proximity of the large export refineries in Colombia, Venezuela

K

and the Netherlands Antilles where the necessary supplies have hitherto been obtained.   However, the need for the development of alternative economic activities to supplement the unhealthy dependence of the countries on the exports of bananas, coffee and cotton (which collectively account for over 80 per cent. of total exports) and the need to reduce the foreign exchange expended in importing petroleum products, whose consumption had been rising rapidly (at about 10 per cent. per

TABLE 11

ESTIMATED CONSUMPTION OF MAIN PETROLEUM PRODUCTS IN CENTRAL AMERICA—1960

(in thousands of metric tons)

	Motor Gasoline	Kerosene	Gas/Diesel Oil	Fuel Oil	Total Demand (including other products)
Guatemala	145	26	62	105	375
El Salvador	95	27	26	100	280
Nicaragua	70	21	75	55	245
Honduras	70	16	75	110	305
Costa Rica	75	11	80	26	225
Totals	455	101	318	396	1430

Source: Oil Trade Journals

annum) and seemed likely to continue to do so, led to a recommendation in 1956 by the Committee for Economic Co-operation in Central America that a regional refinery should be established to provide for the total needs of the area.[10] The delay by the Central American countries in reaching a decision on economic integration, including the whole question of regional industries, has nullified this recommendation, for in the meantime interest in separate refinery construction in the several countries has been increasing under the impact of several different factors (Figure 11).

The rate at which the demand for petroleum products had been increasing was such that new companies were tempted to enter the markets, which had formerly been largely in the hands of associated companies of the Standard Oil Company of New Jersey. An effective way of securing a foothold rather more quickly than by a process of gradually building up a

marketing and distributing network was by means of an offer
to build a refinery. Such an offer was made by Shell, whose
interests in this area had hitherto been limited to Guatemala.
Once this company's plans for a refinery in El Salvador—a
refinery, moreover, of such a size (500,000 tons per annum
capacity) that it was obviously designed to meet the total needs

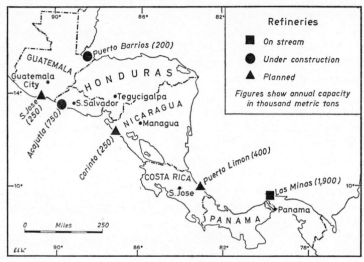

Figure 11. Central America; the Refining Industry

of El Salvador (250,000 tons at the time) and also provide
surpluses available for export to the neighbouring countries—
were announced, there was a two-fold reaction. In the first
place it brought to an end whatever chances there might have
been for an international agreement on refinery construction
in Central America, as it obviously represented a challenge to
the other countries to attempt to secure refinery offers and thus
place them back on an equal footing with El Salvador.
Secondly, the established marketing companies in the area
saw their position being challenged, with the possibility of
their having to accept products made from another company's
crude, and they therefore reacted with plans for defensive
refineries to protect their status. Jersey proposed a second
refinery for El Salvador (of the same capacity as the Shell
project), so that the two projects would have a combined

out-turn some four times the size of El Salvador's requirements. Later Shell and Jersey reached an agreement to build a joint refinery with a capacity about 30 per cent. greater than that proposed for each of the two separate projects. Jersey also offered to build a refinery with a capacity of 250,000 tons in Nicaragua, and in Guatemala Shell took over an even smaller project that was under construction by a firm of United States contractors and made plans to increase its capacity by two and a half times to 500,000 tons. In Costa Rica the government was presented with a series of refinery proposals from no fewer than four companies which generally sought a monopoly position and in return offered such inducements as the construction of a road from Puerto Limón on the Caribbean coast (where the refinery was to be established) to the capital, San José. The offer was not, of course, entirely altruistic in that the centre of gravity of petroleum demand in Costa Rica lies in the Meseta Central region of the country—some 100 miles from the Caribbean coast—and thus a road would have provided a possible means of transporting the products from the refinery or else enabled the refining company to bring such pressure to bear on the railway between Puerto Limón and San José that it would not have been able to charge monopoly tariffs. Most recently, Texaco has made a proposal to build a refinery on Guatemala's Pacific coast, even though the area that such a refinery might be expected to serve is already more than adequately covered by the refineries on Guatemala's Atlantic coast and in neighbouring El Salvador. Only Honduras remains without a firm refinery offer and this omission may well be made good within a short time.

A situation has thus arisen in which these five small Central American republics, with a petroleum demand insufficiently large to support one medium-sized economic refinery, are to have at least five refineries, which although small offer a capacity almost twice the size necessitated by present needs. Although the refineries may be expected to obtain tariff or other effective protection against products from other countries and thus for the time being necessitate the negotiation of inter-company supply agreements so that inter-country trade is more or less eliminated, this situation could be changed if petroleum products are included in the scheme for free trade within the region.*   With free trade there may well arise the further proliferation of oil installations as the marketing companies decide (or are obliged) to take their supplies from the refinery owned by an associated concern in order that the refinery may be used to as near capacity as possible.

A further complicating factor arises from the establishment in Panama of a much larger refinery with a capacity of over 2 million tons per annum.   Though this development is principally related to the markets offered by the bunkering trade at the Panama Canal and to the demand for lighter products on the west coast of the United States, the refinery may well have surplus capacity at least in its early years, which could be employed in manufacturing products for export to other parts of Central America.

The refinery has a two-fold advantage over those in the rest of the area.   One quite obviously arises from the economies of scale that will be achieved in the manufacturing process. The second arises from the fact that it is owned by independent companies which can obtain their crude supplies at less than the posted prices.   They will thus be in a more advantageous position to show refining profits—thus winning greater political acceptance locally by providing a broader tax base for the government—and possibly to offer lower product prices than the refineries associated with the international companies which would, in theory, transfer the crude at posted prices and, in fact, keep the discounts to the minimum necessary to enable their refineries just to break even when selling products at the usual import prices.

The opportunity for this Panamanian refinery to compete for outlets in Central America will, however, arise only if Panama accedes to the Treaty of Economic Integration and thus achieves membership of the proposed Central American Common Market.   Such a move is permitted under the terms of the Treaty.   If Panama remains outside the Common Market it is certain that the products from its refinery will not be allowed to compete with those from the domestic

* Under the Central American Treaty of Economic Integration petroleum products are excluded from the free trade arrangements.   Agreement on the exchange of petroleum products must, however, be reached with in a period of five years after ratification of the Treaty, for a Common Market is then to be established.

refineries, which must be assured of protection from all outside sources of competition. Moreover, it appears that the construction of the small refineries in the Central American countries and the possibility that their products can be under-sold by the more economic Panamanian refinery could now form a serious obstacle to the achievement of greater economic integration between Panama and the other countries. The stake and prestige of the Central American governments tied up in their newly developed refining industries and the powerful interests of the international oil companies, which have indicated their willingness to invest perhaps £25 million in building the refineries to protect their own crude outlets in the area, would together seem to form an effective barrier to whatever hopes the Panamanians may have that their country will become the centre of the refining industry of Central America. Integration proposals will now have to surmount this new development before they are acceptable to all the countries concerned.

Thus, for the countries of Central America whose longer-term needs demand lower production costs in order that the competitiveness of their goods may be enhanced, the establish-ment, in the interests of short-term commercial and political pressures, of local refineries protected against more cheaply produced imports will not help to reduce the prices of petroleum products. It even seems likely that the situation may worsen on two counts. Firstly, the small refineries, which, as already indicated, will need either quota protection or a high tariff protection, may be able to work profitably only if the prices of products are raised above their present levels. Secondly, many of the area's main consumers—such as the companies connected with plantation agriculture and the railways—have been in a position to negotiate at an international rather than at a local level for their relatively large supplies of petroleum products and have secured special terms, at prices below those prevailing locally, for their bulk requirements delivered directly into their own tankage at the major ports. Their privilege of doing this may well be lost once the local refineries are established, for all product imports are likely to be prohibited if similar qualities are available from the local refineries. The companies concerned may thus face significantly higher prices

for their energy requirements and for those trading internationally in highly competitive businesses—for example, the
banana producers—this could well help to make their operations higher cost than those in other parts of the world and thus
lead to retrenchment in their activities.

Having thus examined the rationale behind the development
of the market located refineries in the post-war period, we
must now turn to study the situation of those refineries located
at the source of the crude oil, where the large size of the
individual refineries makes for a low manufacturing cost per
unit of output—an economic advantage which is reinforced
by the fact that natural gas, which is often found in association
with the crude oil that is feeding the refinery and which would
otherwise be 'flared' off owing to the present lack of alternative
uses, can be utilized as a refinery fuel. This is not an insignificant advantage, for refinery use accounts for the equivalent of
about 7 per cent. of the crude imput. These two factors
negative much of the seemingly large saving in transport costs
resulting from moving crude rather than products to the
market and could well have slowed the expansion of market
located refineries if political and strategic factors had not
intervened in favour of the latter.

In round figures, such resource located refineries, which
accounted for about two-thirds of total refinery capacity in
1939, now provide only one-third of the greatly expanded
capacity. It seems, moreover, that there is a degree of surplus
capacity in many of the resource oriented refineries, others of
which—for example, Abadan—have not had their equipment
kept up-to-date and whose ability to meet modern specifications
for products is, therefore, limited. It must be emphasized,
however, that the decline of these refineries has only been
relative to the rest of the industry, for between 1939 and 1961
there has been an actual increase of about 150 per cent. in their
capacity. A most interesting phenomenon is a marked
regional contrast in the pattern of development. This
demands an explanation.

The refineries of the Middle East were expanded most
quickly during the war years and in the immediate post-war
period, with the effect that from 1939 to 1951 total capacity
increased from 16 to 42 million tons per year.[11] This can be

attributed to the wartime extension of refinery capacity in Iran, Palestine, Bahrain, Egypt and Lebanon to supply the allied effort east of Suez and to the further post-war expansions of refineries in a period when there was a world-wide shortage of energy and when every effort had to be made, as far as most of the world was concerned, to secure supplies from non-dollar sources.   Moreover, in this period United States companies were for the first time able to take advantage of the investments they had started to put into the Middle East in the years immediately before the war. Hence refineries were constructed to process crude from the new fields in Saudi Arabia and Qatar. It is logical to regard these almost as pre-war ventures which, therefore, were completed without reference to the changed economic and political conditions of the post-war period.

Since 1951, however, there has been little expansion of Middle East refinery capacity, and indeed during this period the world's largest refinery at Abadan was out of action for three years following the nationalization of the Anglo-Iranian Oil Company in 1951. Abadan's peak capacity figure of 25 million tons in 1950 has not been used again and its throughput is now at a post-crisis peak of about 20 million tons. However, the period of stagnation in refinery growth in the area may be nearing its end, for four projects have recently been announced which, when completed, will increase capacity by almost 11 million tons a year.

In this development it is possible to discern a politico-economic reaction by the Middle Eastern countries to their unsatisfactory status as merely primary producing nations. Although the profits of the oil industry are, as a result of the posted price policy of the major integrated companies, largely concentrated at the producing stage[12] (profits in which the host governments share by virtue of royalty and other tax payments—see Chapter 8), Middle Eastern governments have, until recently, generally felt that they were losing revenue by failing to participate in refining operations which, they have assumed, must be profitable. Additional refinery capacity, moreover, in addition to thus providing them with higher revenues, also provides more employment opportunities and is something of a status symbol. Thus, Iraq plans to build a 1·3 million ton state-owned refinery with technical and financial assistance from Czechoslovakia.   The Saudi Arabian government has authorized a local company to build a 1 million ton refinery; and, in Kuwait, the American independent company, Aminoil, is increasing the capacity of its refinery from 2 to 7·5 million tons.   In addition, the Kuwait Oil Company (Gulf–B.P.) is to increase its refinery capacity by 3 million tons.   Aminoil's very significant development may perhaps reflect company fears of difficulties in getting rid of its increasing output of crude.   It has no marketing facilities outside the United States (except for a small prospective crude outlet to the proposed Rhodesian refinery) and is restricted in its sales to the United States by the import quotas imposed on foreign crude.   The decision to secure a greater availability of products by increasing refining capacity was probably made in the hope that the company will thereby have greater opportunities to find outlets for its increasing production. Large consumers can perhaps be found in various parts of the Eastern Hemisphere who would not refuse the opportunity to buy petroleum products at less than those posted at the Persian Gulf by the international companies which, it has been suggested, are based on an 'outdated product-pricing formula'.[13]

Further extensions of the refining facilities in the Middle East may also be expected as a result of agreements reached during the hectic competition for concessions in the 1950s. In order to make their offers as attractive as possible, many companies seeking exploration rights offered to build refineries under certain conditions—usually at the time that production from a concession reaches a certain level.   The Japanese owned Arabian Oil Company, which secured the Kuwait–Saudi Arabian Neutral Zone off-shore concession, agreed to build a refinery as soon as production reached an annual level of 1·5 million tons for a consecutive period of 90 days.   This level of production is likely to be achieved during 1963, and it seems that plans for the refinery are already being considered.*   In Iran the off-shore concession agreements made with E.N.I. and Pan-American in 1957 and 1958 (both in conjunction with the National Iranian Oil Company) implied that future consideration would be given to the possibilities of building

---

* It was, however, reported in June, 1962 that the Japanese company is endeavouring to postpone its obligations to build a refinery.

refinery capacity. Even Shell, which as one of the major international companies endeavours to retain as free a hand as possible in deciding refinery location so that its refining capacity may be matched to the company's supply and the world demand pattern, felt constrained to offer the Kuwait government co-operation 'in respect of tanker transport and in other sectors of the industry' in order to secure the important and attractive off-shore territory in 1961. This could well be interpreted quite fairly to imply consideration for the possibilities of refinery construction.

In great contrast with this timing of refinery expansion in the Middle East, the other main area of resource located refineries —the Caribbean complex of Venezuela, Colombia, Trinidad and the Netherlands Antilles—showed a period of relatively slow growth from 35 million tons in 1939 to 50 million tons in 1951. Since 1951, however, there has been a decade of large-scale developments which have increased capacity to 86 million tons. Thus, while the percentage of the world's total refining capacity located in the Caribbean producing area fell from more than 37 per cent. in 1939 to only 23 per cent. in 1951, the relative decline since then has been very much slower and by 1961 the area still had 18 per cent. of the world total. The main reason for this seems to be the changing pattern of exports from the Caribbean. Even in the late 1940s Western Europe was still taking greater amounts of Caribbean products than immediately before the war in spite of the need to conserve dollars (viz. 15 million tons in 1947 compared with 10 million tons in 1938. This increase in Europe's offtake, together with an increase of the same order of magnitude in product exports to the rest of South America (from 4 to 9 million tons), had occasioned the gradual development of refinery capacity, particularly in Venezuela, where the government had in 1943 insisted that concessionaires must refine at least 15 per cent. of their crude output in the country. (Previously nearly all of Venezuela's output had been processed in the Netherlands Antilles.)[14] Increased exports to North America in this period had been principally as crude (from 4 million tons in 1938 to 17 million tons in 1947), this outlet for products having increased only from 3·5 to 8·0 million tons.[15]

After this period, however, as European refining expanded

and as Europe turned to an increasing degree to non-dollar oil, the Caribbean refining industry's fortunes became more closely tied with the rapidly expanding demand of the North American market. The United States' rising import needs increased the potential crude outlet for the Caribbean, but of equal significance was the move by the United States refiners to produce an increasing gasoline yield as a means of maximizing their returns on investment. Large parts of the eastern United States became deficient in residual oil as east coast refiners reduced their output of residual oil from 21·7 per cent. of output in 1949 to 10·5 per cent. by 1958.[16] This was particularly marked in the winter months and the Venezuelan and the other Caribbean refineries were expanded to fill this market, which was, moreover, enlarged as cheaper imported fuel oil displaced increasing quantities of coal. Residual oil imports into the eastern United States increased by 10 million tons (from 6 to 16·5 million) between 1946 and 1950 and by another 10 million tons by 1958, when they provided over 40 per cent. of the total requirements of the area. It was largely to meet this expanding market that the Caribbean refineries were developed in the period after 1950.

More recently, the United States' import restrictions have virtually frozen imports of residual fuel oil at their 1957 level (though there were some upward adjustments in 1962). This, together with the loss of product outlets in Latin America, where, as already demonstrated, the consuming countries have been building their own refineries, seems likely to restrict any further expansion of refinery capacity in the Caribbean. In fact, some of the expansion projects of the late 1950s have been made superfluous by these developments. The refining industry of the Caribbean export complex, therefore, which in the last decade has added more capacity than any other area in the non-communist world outside the United States except for Western Europe, now appears to be approaching a period of stagnation unless and until the United States permits greatly increased imports of residual oil. For this reason—and also because, as already shown, there are factors favouring expansion of refining capacity in the Middle East—it seems that the 1960s will see a significant narrowing of the gap of some 40 million tons per annum in refining capacity that now exists between the two major exporting areas of the world. There will thus be yet another decade of differential development in the refining industry of the two areas—perhaps as significant a phenomenon as that of the much more widely discussed concept of the 'move to the market' by the refining industry.

REFERENCES

1 N. S. Ginsburg. *An Atlas of Economic Development*, 1961, p. 86.

2 S. H. Longrigg. *Oil in the Middle East*, 2nd Edition, 1961, pp. 129 and 103.

3 R. C. Estall and R. O. Buchanan. *Industrial Activity and Economic Geography*, 1961, pp. 210–223.

4 P. H. Frankel and W. L. Newton. 'The Location of Refineries.' *Institute of Petroleum Review*. Vol. 15, No. 175, July 1961.

5 A. Melamid. 'Geographical Distribution of Petroleum Refining Capacities.' *Economic Geography*. Vol. 31, No. 2, 1955, p. 168.

6 P. H. Frankel. 'Oil Supplies in the Suez Crisis.' *Journal of Industrial Economics*. Vol. IV, No. 2, February 1958, p. 100.

7 *Petroleum Press Service*. October 1950, p. 273.

8 P. H. Frankel and W. L. Newton. *Op. cit.*

9 From information supplied by one of the major oil companies.

10 This recommendation was, however, made on the assumption that a refinery of 500,000 tons annual capacity would be an economic proposition. See 'La Integracion Economica de Centoamerica'. *U.N. Economic and Social Council*, November, 1956, p. 34.

11 P. H. Frankel and W. L. Newton. *Op. cit.*, p. 200.

12 See E. Penrose. 'Middle East Oil: The International Distribution of Profits and Income Tax.' *Economica*. Vol. XXVII, No. 107, August 1960, p. 203.

13 W. A. Leeman. *The Price of Middle Eastern Oil*, 1962, p. 108.

14 E. Lieuwen. *Venezuela*, 1961, p. 115.

15 W. E. Pratt and D. Good (Ed.). 'World Geography of Petroleum.' *A.G.S. Special Publication*, No. 31, p. 407.

16 W. J. Levy. *Oil and Gas in the B.T.U. Battle*. Report prepared for the Pontiac Refining Corp., 1959, p. 22.

CHAPTER 7

Transport and Distribution

The transport requirements of the petroleum industry fall into three main categories. The most significant of the three in tonnage and in the distances involved is the movement of crude oil from the points of production to the refineries. Of secondary importance is the transport of products from the export refineries to the marketing areas. And, finally, there is the much smaller scale movement of products from market located refineries, ocean terminals or other similar bulk installations to the final consumer. This presentation does, of course, represent a greatly simplified breakdown of the actual situation, for the three different types of movement do not fall into a distinct geographical pattern. In total, therefore, the requirements of the industry present a complex picture which is illustrated diagrammatically in Figure 12.

There are several main reasons for this complexity. In the first place, there is a constantly changing demand for oil products. This demand each individual company must seek to serve with a minimum investment in both installations and transport. For example, a market located refinery built to serve the forecast needs of an area may be temporarily unable to supply a higher than estimated demand for a particular product. In such a case, the company concerned will be obliged to send in additional supplies of that product from a refinery located elsewhere. On the other hand, a refinery may find itself with capacity surplus to local requirements and the company will then need to find an alternative outlet elsewhere. In India, for example, the structure of demand for petroleum products is such that gasoline is normally available for re-export from the refineries fed in the first place with crude imported from the Middle East. It is in cases such as this that the refineries owned by the international oil companies are at an advantage compared with those under national ownership for whereas the latter have specifically to seek an outlet needing the particular product in surplus and thus possibly have to sell at distress rates, the products from the former can be incorporated into the overall supply pattern of the company concerned.

The complexity of the world pattern of oil transport also arises from the great diversity in ownership of production and

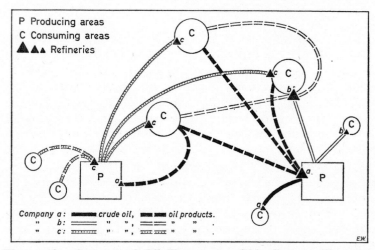

Figure 12.   Patterns of Oil Transport.   This diagram illustrates the complexity of transport requirements which arise from the multiplicity and diverse ownership of oil producing, refining and distributing facilities

refining facilities.   One company's transport pattern differs from another's because of the varied distribution of producing and refining facilities.   For example, while most of the United Kingdom's petroleum requirements are transported in the form of crude from the Middle East and the Caribbean, the Regent Petroleum Company, without refining facilities in the country in 1962 (although the possibilities for building a refinery at Milford Haven were then being examined), has continued to meet the demand by transporting products from refineries of the controlling companies (Texaco and Caltex) in Trinidad, the Middle East and European countries.   In Scandinavia, most international companies have established refineries designed to serve their markets in more than one country.

The Esso refinery to the south of Oslo in Norway, for example, also provides products to the Danish company while Shell plan to serve their Norwegian outlets from a refinery in Denmark. Thus, only if the petroleum industry were 'internationalized' with a central planning organization to arrange transport without reference to the individual ownership of oil and facilities, would this factor not continue to complicate the pattern of oil transport.

Two outstanding manifestations of the impact of the factor are the passage in *both* directions along the Suez and the Panama canals of tankers loaded with crude oil. In 1961, 105 million tons of crude moved northward through Suez, mainly from the Middle East to Europe; in the opposite direction over 3 million tons of Russian crude went through the Canal on its way to Japan. Through the Panama Canal the main movement is from east to west—the transport of Caribbean crude to the west coast of the United States—but in the reverse direction some Peruvian crude moves to the United Kingdom refinery of the company concerned.

Even in the abnormal conditions pertaining at the time of the Suez crisis, the supply of essential oil to Western Europe could only be achieved largely within the framework of company rather than of industry facilities. In his analysis of the pattern of oil supplies during the crisis, P. H. Frankel has noted that the redirection of tankers was 'so slowed down by the time it took to work out the considerable number of complicated individual deals between the partners (in the emergency programme) in the commercial give and take of which the process consisted that it was not until some months after the closing of the canal that the movement of Middle East crudes to the western hemisphere was materially reduced . . . that right through the crisis tankers carried oil out of the Mediterranean to faraway destinations, whereas others took oil into the Mediterranean . . . and that too much Venezuelan crude continued to be sent to the United States instead of to Europe'.[1]

Bearing in mind, therefore, that there are factors which make for a high degree of complexity in the detailed pattern of oil transport, we can now turn to an examination of the most significant aspects. Figure 13 shows the major inter-regional movements of crude oil in 1961. Out of a total movement of

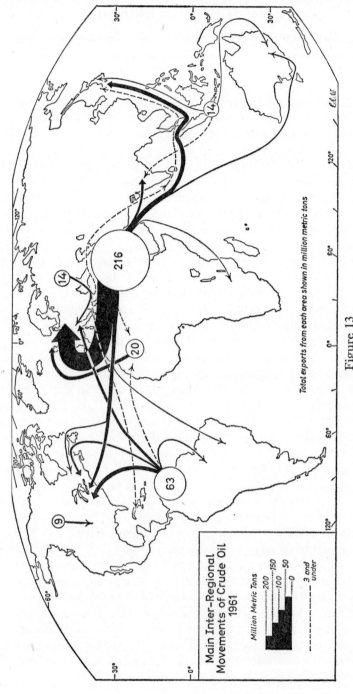

Main Inter-Regional
Movements of Crude Oil
1961

Million Metric Tons

200—150
100— 50
3 and
under
0

Total exports from each area shown in million metric tons

Figure 13

about 325 million tons, about two-thirds originated in the Middle East and of this more than 60 per cent. moved to Western Europe.   In contrast with this major route, most other movements appear relatively insignificant.   The two next most important are from the Caribbean to the east coast of North America and from the Middle East to the Far East.   Although the two routes account for much the same tonnage at the moment, it should be noted that whereas the growth of traffic on the former has slowed down as a result of slower rate of increase in demand for petroleum in the United States and Canada, the impact of United States' import restrictions and increasing competition from Middle Eastern supplies, the traffic on the latter route has grown even more quickly in importance than that on the Middle East–Western Europe route, largely through increasing exports to Japan, whose off-take of Middle Eastern crude has expanded from 1·5 million tons in 1951* to 22 million tons in 1960.

There have been two recent developments in the movement of crude which are likely to continue to increase in importance. The first is the movement from the Middle East across the Atlantic to both North and South America.   In 1961, these two areas received 23 million tons and 5 million tons of crude oil respectively from the Middle East.   This development is in response to the availability of Middle Eastern crude at f.o.b. prices much lower than those charged for equivalent qualities of Venezuelan oil and the ability of importers to secure low freight rates because of an over-supply of tankers.   Thus, Middle East oil has a c.i.f. advantage over Venezuelan supplies over most of the east coasts of both North and South America. The point at which the delivered prices of oil from the two sources is competitive has, in fact, been steadily moving westward during much of the post-war period, but it is only since the late 1950s that it has moved sufficiently far to make growth of this particular route of significance.

The second development has been the growth in the movement of crude from Soviet Black Sea ports.   In 1960 this totalled less than 10 million tons but the amount shipped practically doubled in 1961.   Much of the movement has been

* The first full year that imports of crude were permitted after the war.   (See p. 121.)

L

over relatively short distances into Western Europe, but 1961 exports to both Cuba (over 3 million tons) and Japan (over 3 million tons) form the basis of a longer distance crude transport pattern. The shipments to Japan—which are likely to continue to increase until the trans-Siberian crude pipeline is completed—give rise, as already noted, to the unusual north–south movement of loaded crude tankers of up to 48,000 tons through the Suez canal. The westward movement of Soviet crude to Cuba may soon be supplemented by shipments to Brazil, which has signed an agreement to import some of its requirements from the U.S.S.R.

Elsewhere the inter-regional movements of crude oil are essentially local. The producing areas of Indonesia and Borneo export mainly to Australasia, Japan and South-East Asian refineries. North African crude moves into Western Europe at the moment, although as production increases it is possible that it may be shipped to the United States, where the demand for various products matches much more closely the yield of products obtained by the distillation of the light Saharan crudes. Eastern Europe's modest needs are filled by Rumanian and Soviet crudes. The Caribbean's exports of crude to areas outside the western hemisphere are relatively small, although there has recently been some revival in the flow of Venezuelan crude to Western Europe. This arises from the fact that the demand for fuel oil in Western Europe has been increasing more rapidly than the demand for other products and, thus, the heavier Venezuelan crudes, which yield a higher proportion of fuel oil, are needed to supplement the limited supplies of this type of crude from the Middle East and also to mix with the light Saharan crudes. New producers in Venezuela have also been obliged to turn to Europe for alternative outlets for their production in the face of the United States import quotas against them (see page 37). Subsidiary movements from the Middle East supply much of the crude demand in Africa, Asia and Australasia. One negative aspect of the pattern should not be overlooked. This is the absence of crude movements from the United States, which, in spite of maintaining its position as the world's most important oil producer, is now second only to Western Europe as a whole in the amount of crude it imports.

Crude supplies are moved to refineries by a combination of pipeline and ocean tanker transport, the relative use of each means varying according to locational and economic factors. Until recent developments, the pipeline transport of crude outside North America was restricted to the movement of the oil from the producing fields to the coastally located refineries or to major exporting terminals.*

The lines from the producing areas usually transport the oil to the nearest point on the coast at which a terminal or refinery either is available or can be built. Figure 14 shows, for example, the network of lines leading from the various fields in Iran to Abadan. The northern fields—Masjid-i-Sulaiman, Naft Safid, Haft Kel, etc.—were the first to be developed and Abadan was the most convenient location for the export refinery. The more southerly fields (at Agha Jari and Gach Saran) were later tied in to the facilities at Abadan, whose facilities were expanded to take increasing quantities of oil, and to a new crude oil terminal at Mashur. A combination of several factors, however, including rising production, navigational limitations in the Shatt-el Arab and difficulties in the Khor Musa for the larger and larger tankers used for crude transport, the greater emphasis on crude than on product exports and the development of pipeline technology to make lengthy under-water lines possible, has led to the construction of an additional export terminal on Kharg Island, twenty-two miles off the Iranian mainland and some 130 miles south-east of Abadan. The output of the Gach Saran field (mainly responsible for Iran's rising production since 1960) which, except for 3 million tons a year suitable for bitumen manufacture at Abadan, is to be exported as crude rather than processed locally, will be channelled through the new facilities, which reduce the pipeline transit from 150 to 100 miles and at the same time save the tankers a day's passage because of the lesser distance that they have to travel.

In Kuwait, the prolific Burgan field is located within a few

* It should, however, be remembered that in an earlier period of oil industry development before pipeline technology was sufficiently advanced, refineries were built even on interior oilfields in order to minimize the problem of crude transport. This is seen, for example, in the location of three refineries in the interior of Iraq in the immediate vicinity of the fields which were first exploited in the 1930s. These are shown on Figure 14.

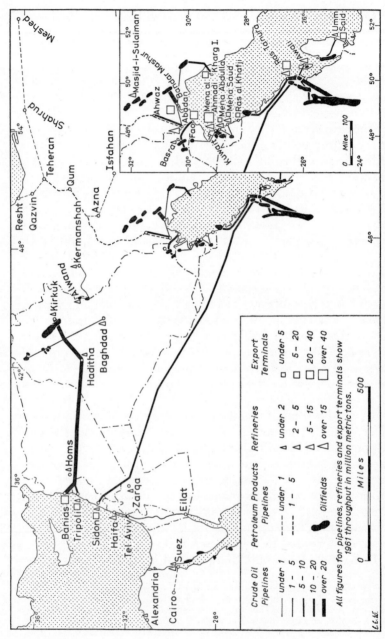

Figure 14. The Middle East; Refineries, Terminals and Pipelines

miles of the coast which, moreover, has provided suitable sites for large-scale ocean installations. The development of the off-shore facilities by the Japanese similarly involves limited pipeline transport to a terminal which is under construction at Ras al Khafji on the mainland. Figure 14 also brings out the suitable location of most of the Saudi Arabian fields for exporting through the facilities at Ras Tanura. It is significant that the more remote Safaniya field has also been connected by pipeline with Ras Tanura even though its own location is coastal and off-shore. The absence of separate export facilities arises in part from the physical difficulties of developing a terminal at the field, and in part from the fact that the same company has been responsible for developing this field and may, therefore, have considered it more economic to expand existing facilities and to build the crude pipeline rather than make the investment in separate exporting and tanker handling facilities, which additionally would not have given the alternative refining opportunities that exist at Ras Tanura. The field was, moreover, a relatively small producer—a maximum of under 4 million tons—until 1961. The rapid expansion of the field since then (production in 1962 was about 16 million tons) and the discovery of other fields in the same vicinity might, however, eventually make a separate terminal desirable.

Figure 15 illustrates the pattern of crude oil pipelines from field to export point or refinery in Venezuela and Colombia. The older refineries such as San Roque and Oficina were located on the fields but have long since been overshadowed by the development of coastal facilities, such as those at Cardón and Mene Grande, fed by a complex of crude oil lines from the various producing fields. Two developments indicate the general tendency to keep the length of these lines to a minimum. In the west of the country it has been considered worthwhile to spend some £13 million on deepening the entrance to Lake Maracaibo so that the crude can be delivered into the tankers at the point of production thus eliminating the 150-mile pipeline journey to the terminals on the Paraguana peninsula. In the east the development of the Morichal field, has led Phillips Petroleum Company to build a pipeline to a terminal on the Orinoco River rather than to one on the north coast thereby reducing the overland pipeline transport

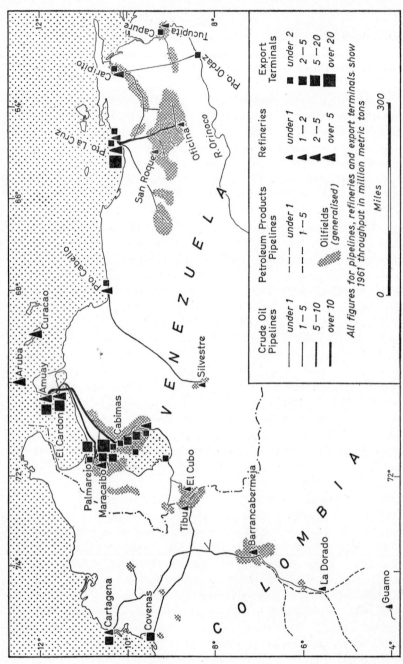

Figure 15. Pipelines, Refineries and Terminals in Venezuela and Colombia

from over 150 to 42 miles. These Venezuelan examples would, therefore, seem to confirm the general principle that pipelines in producing areas are used only to get the crude to the nearest possible export point where ocean tankers—a cheaper and more flexible form of transport—can take over.

Exceptions to this principle are found when additional pipeline construction saves tanker transport over a much greater distance. The most outstanding examples of this are the pipelines from Iraq and Saudi Arabia to the Eastern Mediterranean. In the late 1930s the development of the fields in north-east Iraq was creating problems in the transport of products from the local refineries. An increase in the capacity of the line running to Baghdad and its extension to the head of the Persian Gulf would have represented the shortest route to ocean transport facilities but instead the somewhat longer pipeline routes to Tripoli in the Lebanon and Haifa in Palestine were chosen even though this development also imposed additional legal complications and additional royalty obligations in securing agreement with the two countries through which the lines were to pass. The extra 100–200 miles of pipelines, however, secured a saving of more than 4000 miles of tanker transport. Thus, a tanker employed in carrying products to Western Europe would be able to make almost twice as many voyages a year. The economic advantage of this use of pipeline rather than tanker transport is readily apparent and the capacity of the northern line has been increased from its original figure of 2 million tons per annum to over 45 million tons. In part, this has been to compensate for the closure of the southern section of the line to Haifa following the establishment of the state of Israel, through which no Arab oil was permitted to pass (an event which illustrates the inflexibility of investment in pipelines compared with that in tankers), but in much greater part to permit an expansion of Iraqi production.

The line from Saudi Arabia to the Mediterranean, Tapline, was conceived in the late 1940s and finally completed in 1950. The 1200-mile line, whose throughput originates within a few miles of the ocean terminals on the Persian Gulf, cost an estimated £80 million to construct and its running costs include the maintenance of thirteen—for the most part isolated—pumping stations. The line was originally built because it was cheaper to move the oil 1200 miles by pipeline rather than about 3500 miles by ocean tanker around Arabia and through the Suez Canal. Since the late 1950s, however, the pipeline seems to have lost its advantage. This is the result of several developments. The cost of tanker operation has been greatly reduced by the increasing size of vessels. It has been estimated, for example, that a 65,000-ton tanker can transport oil at 56 per cent. of the cost of using a 16,000-ton vessel (the standard size until the post-war era). Moreover, since 1958 actual tanker freight rates—particularly for large tankers—have been seriously depressed as a result of excess capacity. During this period, too, new markets have been opened for Saudi Arabian oil in the western hemisphere—on these voyages the pipeline does not give such a large percentage saving in mileage as it does on the route to Europe. As a result of these developments the use made of Tapline declined to only half its capacity of about 24 million tons a year. By contrast, tankers from Ras Tanura on the Persian Gulf are now lifting well over 20 million tons of crude a year compared with only 15 million tons in 1957. Thus, in this case, even where great mileage savings are effected by the use of pipelines, tanker transport has reasserted its attraction and re-emphasized that the prime function of crude lines in producing areas is to take the oil to the nearest convenient loading point for ocean transportation.

The most recent developments in the use of pipelines for crude oil movement have taken place at the market end of the supply route. Whereas market located refineries have previously been located at tidewater (see Figures 7 and 8 showing the location of refineries in Europe) so that ocean tankers could discharge their cargoes directly into the tank farm, there is now a move to locate refineries in the heart of major consuming areas. This sometimes involves moving the oil by pipeline from the import terminal. The development is again most apparent where such a project saves a considerable amount of ocean transport. Alsace, Lorraine, Bavaria and northern Switzerland, for example, have been supplied with petroleum products shipped inland by river, canal or rail, from refineries on the Dutch and German coasts. These areas are now, however, to be supplied by local refineries, located at Strasbourg, Ingolstadt and Karlsruhe, which will draw their crude intake by pipelines from ocean terminals at Marseilles and Genoa. The line from Marseilles to Strasbourg and Ingolstadt will be over 500 miles long but it will save some 3500 miles of tanker transport via the Straits of Gibraltar and the English Channel to a Dutch or German refinery and some 400 miles of product transport by inland waterway or railway. The changing combinations of tanker and pipeline transport for crude oil moving from the Persian Gulf to these parts of Western Europe are set out in Table 12.

TABLE 12

MOVEMENT OF CRUDE OIL—
SAUDI ARABIA TO WESTERN EUROPE

	Miles by Ocean Tanker	Miles by Pipeline	Additional Product mileage to South Germany
Pre Trans-Arabian Pipeline	6600	..	400
Tapline—Sidon–North Germany	3365	1200	400
Tapline — Sidon–Marseilles–Strasbourg–Ingolstadt	1600	1750	Local Distribution only

It is conceivable that the further growth of intensive markets in other parts of Western Europe accompanied by further improvements in pipeline technology could lead to the future development of other crude line facilities. It might, for example, become economic to establish a refinery in the Paris area (now fed with products from the coastal refineries at Le Havre and Rouen) based on crude delivered by pipeline from the Mediterranean coast. In fact, a mere 300-mile branch line from the South European line near Lyons to Paris would eliminate a 4500-mile round trip journey by ocean tanker. Similarly, a continuation of the lines from Marseilles or Genoa to the Baltic coast—an additional distance of about 550 miles from the Karlsruhe terminal in South Germany—might provide an alternative route for the crude moving to the refineries in Scandinavia. This alternative would save almost 5000 miles of tanker transport.

The communist countries, which have introduced a considerable degree of joint planning into their programmes for energy production and consumption, are on the point of completing the most important pipeline complex for crude oil anywhere in the world.   To a very large degree (as described in Chapter 2), the East European countries are dependent on the Soviet Union for their oil supplies.   For East Germany, Poland, Czechoslovakia, and Hungary this dependence has involved receiving their oil supplies mainly by rail transport over a distance of more than 1500 miles.   The only alternative routes have involved a combination of pipeline, rail and barge transport from the main Volga-Urals fields to the Black Sea and thence by barge up the Danube or by tanker around Western Europe to the Baltic ports.   The latter route has also had to be used for crude exported to the countries of Western Europe.   In the light of the high cost of the rail movement of crude and the much longer distances involved in the alternative means of transport, the communist countries jointly agreed to construct the so-called 'Friendship' pipeline from the Volga-Urals fields to the refineries in Poland, East Germany, Hungary and Czechoslovakia with another branch of the line to the Baltic coast of the U.S.S.R. where there is to be a terminal for exports to Scandinavia.   Soviet experts have indicated that transport costs will be reduced by 75 per cent. as a result of the construction of the line, which will be the longest in the world.   With a diameter of forty inches over much of its length (and even thirty-six inches at the terminal points) it will also have a larger capacity than any other line in the world and by 1965 will be delivering about 50 million tons of crude oil a year to the refineries and export terminals.   It will be noted that one of its terminals—at Bratislava in Czechoslovakia—is only a short distance from Vienna, which is to be the terminal of a crude oil line from the head of the Adriatic Sea and it is possible that a connecting link will eventually be built so that Soviet crude can be delivered directly to Italy—which has signed large long-term contracts for buying Soviet oil—and thus provide an alternative to the present tanker transport from the Black Sea ports.   The offer by the Soviet Union in 1961 to construct a refinery in Bavaria can also be viewed in the light of the pipeline project, which would only have needed to be extended by 250 miles to provide the supply of crude oil. (The offer was rejected by the West German government under pressure from the United States.)

A Soviet pipeline project of even greater magnitude is under construction. This is the extension of the line from the Volga-Urals fields, at present running as far as Irkutsk, to the Pacific coast near Vladivostock. When completed in the late 1960s the total length of the line will be over 4000 miles and it will be capable of delivering 20 million tons a year to the terminal. In part the line is to provide oil for the expanding needs of eastern Siberia, which is planned to develop into a new industrial region, but it will also serve as an export terminal for crude oil destined for Japan, to which the Soviet Union hopes to export some 10 million tons of oil annually. Thus, the 4000-mile pipeline and a short tanker haul will replace the present difficult overland route to the Black Sea and the 10,000 mile tanker route via Suez. Because of the length of this route, the present return to the Soviet Union at the port of origin for oil sold to Japan is only about $1.00 per barrel (only two-thirds the size of its return for most of its sales in Western Europe) and is probably accepted only because of the Soviet Union's need to build up its outlet in Japan so that the pipeline can be fully utilized as soon as it is completed.

The construction of these internationally significant pipelines within the communist countries serves to illustrate that even with different economic principles from those under which the oil industry operates in the rest of the world, pipeline transport for crude may well become economic when its use thereby obviates the need for a much longer journey by ocean tanker. The location of the main Soviet fields (see Chapter 2, page 18) in the interior of the Eurasian land mass, however, is a particularly appropriate one for the development of pipeline transport, and the international lines are really only rather limited extensions of projects which are needed to supply oil to the major consuming regions of the Soviet Union itself. Moreover, in that exports to Eastern and Western Europe and to Japan provide the higher demand that makes the capital expenditure on the pipelines worthwhile, these extensions can be viewed as an integral part of the Soviet oil supply system and help to provide the basis on which Soviet refineries can be located in relation to the local markets. Were it not for the fact that exports will provide the additional throughput needed to make the long crude oil lines an economic undertaking, it seems possible that the eastern and the western parts of the Soviet Union remote from the areas of oil production might well have had their oil requirements met by rail-moved products for some considerable time ahead.

The similarity between this situation and that in Canada where the main producing areas are also located in the relatively remote continental interior is significant. The major consuming area of eastern Canada is over 2000 miles away and in spite of a highly intensive demand in this area it has been considered uneconomic to build a crude line to Montreal as there were no intermediate areas in Canada to provide additional significant outlets and no opportunities for exporting just across the border from the Montreal area. In this it contrasts with the Soviet Union. It has been only with the possibility of building a pipeline with a greater diameter, designed to serve parts of the northern United States on its way eastwards, that the cost of transporting the crude can be reduced sufficiently to enable it to be delivered at a price at which it might compete in the refineries of Montreal with oil imported from Venezuela and the Middle East.

In contrast with the developing situation in both the Soviet Union and Canada, the crude pipelines in the United States are mainly concerned with moving the crude to the nearest ocean terminal. This is so in spite of the great wartime development of the crude pipeline system to avoid the use of tankers which were needed for use elsewhere in the world and which were, of course, susceptible to enemy action. Tankers now take 90 per cent. of the crude oil moving from the Gulf to the east coast whilst the former crude oil lines have been utilized to transport natural gas.

Finally, in the movement of crude oil by pipeline there has recently been a development at the import terminals in the main consuming areas. This arises from the increasing size of crude oil tankers. The largest are already of 115,000 tons, orders have been placed for 130,000 tonners and the forecast is for tankers of 200,000 tons or more.[2] The prospects of finding berthing facilities for these giants in juxtaposition with suitable site requirements and market conditions for the location of refineries are thus growing more remote, and hence new pipelines are being constructed for linking up the crude oil import terminal with the refining point.   Examples of this in the United Kingdom are found at the Grangemouth, the Llandarcy and the Stanlow refineries, which can no longer receive their crude supplies from tankers lying alongside. Grangemouth now receives its crude supplies by a thirty-five-mile pipeline from the tanker terminal on the west coast of Scotland at Finnart, where tankers of over 100,000 tons can discharge their cargoes.   Similarly, the terminal at Milford Haven, also capable of handling the largest tankers in use, feeds the Llandarcy refinery, fifty miles to the east.   The Manchester Ship Canal cannot handle tankers of more than 32,000 tons and thus the Stanlow refinery built alongside it now receives its oil from the new terminal on the Mersey estuary at Tranmere, where 75,000-ton tankers can be handled. The further expected growth in the size of tankers may push the ocean terminal for Stanlow away to Anglesey with a pipeline connection of some 105 miles.   In each case, the development has been needed for refineries already in existence and a similar development seems likely for the Thames-side refineries which cannot accept tankers of more than 45,000 tons. It may, however, foreshadow the construction of a refinery in the heart of the Midlands, as site and water needs are little more exacting than those for large power stations, which are being developed in large numbers along the banks of the Trent and other rivers.   With more intensive consumption the amount of oil required within a forty- to fifty-mile radius of such a refinery could justify its construction in this area with the feedstock brought in by a pipeline little longer than that which may be needed to feed Stanlow.   It would seem in fact that the main consideration delaying the construction of a refinery in the Midlands is not the cost of taking in the crude but rather the additional expense of redistributing products surplus to local demand, which from a coastal refinery move mainly by sea to other parts of the country.

Thus, the economics of large tankers which, we have previously noted, has occasioned such savings in the movement of oil that it is now cheaper to ship by super-tanker around Arabia or even around the Cape of Good Hope, are, at the other end of the journey, beginning to lead to the development of pipelines for crude in the major consuming areas. This provides a good example of the impact of technical change on the economic geography of oil.

The inter-regional transport of petroleum products from the export refineries to the countries in which they are to be marketed is, by tonnage, only half the size of the movement of crude. Moreover, as a comparison of Figures 13 and 16 will bring out, the main route for the movement of products, from the Caribbean to the east coast of the United States, is less than one-third the length of the main route for crude oil from the Middle East to Europe. For reasons which were analyzed in Chapter 6 (see page 142) the refineries of the Caribbean expanded quite significantly in the 1950s and about 50 per cent. of the total exports of oil from that area are still in the form of products, with the main stream northwards to the United States, but with a not unimportant transatlantic movement. This transatlantic movement is caused by three factors. In part it represents the movement necessary to balance the pattern of supply of companies refining the bulk of their European demand at local refineries. In part it is a movement to supply products to companies such as Gulf Oil and Texaco, which have recently expanded their marketing cover in Western Europe and have not yet sufficient outlets to justify the construction of refineries in all the major European countries. In part it is a movement of special products, the full range of which can be produced economically only in the largest refineries, such as those at Cardon in Venezuela and Pointe à Pierre in Trinidad. It seems reasonable to anticipate that there will be a continued demand for movements of this kind and it appears likely to continue to be based on the Caribbean export complex, as long as the latter's primary *raison d'être*—the need for residual oil in the eastern United States—is maintained.

From the Middle East the export of products is only one-seventh the size of crude exports and there is, moreover, a significant difference in the direction of movement. In contrast with the dominating crude route to Western Europe, most

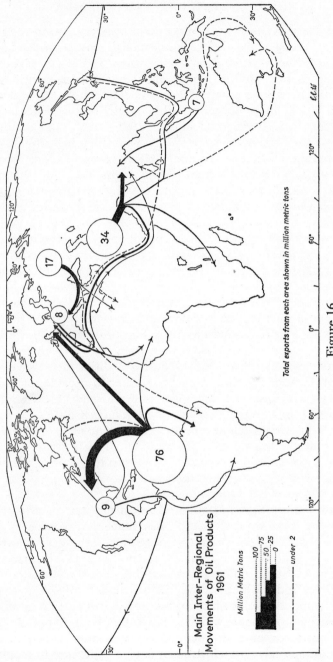

Main Inter-Regional
Movements of Oil Products
1961

Million Metric Tons

100
75
50
25
0

under 2

Total exports from each area shown in million metric tons

Figure 16

products move into areas other than Western Europe. This reflects the fact that there are still many countries in Asia and Africa without refining facilities. Even India, for example, still needed in 1960 to import about one-third of its product requirements. In part this is simply the continuation of the traditional pattern of supplying the smaller markets from large, resource located refineries but in part it is also related to the structure of Indian demand, which with a heavy emphasis on the middle distillates—kerosene and diesel oil—cannot appropriately be met entirely from national refineries. Any attempt to do so would produce a surplus of both fuel oil and gasoline, which would be difficult to dispose of to markets necessarily distant.

Product movements also originate in areas from which there are no exports of crude. This is particularly so in Western Europe, where the refineries are to some degree export refineries, particularly for intra-European trade. (This is not shown on Figure 16, which deals only with inter-regional movements.) Refineries such as Pernis in Holland and many of the Italian refineries export products to other European countries. Such intra-European trade also arises from the fact that some companies concentrate their refining facilities for a group of countries in one of their number in order to provide scope for at least a medium-sized refinery (see also page 115). Some exports from Europe, however, go even further afield, particularly into Africa. This reflects former colonial ties by which the metropolitan powers had preferential tariff treatment for their exports to the colonies. The surplus Italian refining capacity is also conveniently located to export products to many of the small African markets.

The United States also figures as an exporter of products. Some of these exports arise from commercial reasons—from the availability of special products for favourably located markets—but others are related to the overseas requirements of United States military bases and to the foreign aid programme, under which oil supplies are made available to some of the under-developed countries. As a result of increasing balance of payments difficulties for the United States, the administrators of both the military and the economic aid programmes have been instructed to give preference to supplies from the United States even though these may be obtainable only at prices higher than those for similar products from other countries. For example, United States aid to the West African country of Mali included an agreement to provide oil products. Even though the companies concerned with supplying Mali shipped some of the requirements from associated European refineries of the same international group, this pattern is not permitted under the United States aid programme, which can insist on products being transported from the United States.

Because of the trend, analyzed in Chapter 6, towards the growth of refinery capacity in consuming rather than in producing areas, the movement of products from export refineries will grow much less quickly than the movement of crude. It should be borne in mind, however, that the refineries in the producing areas will continue to operate and to expand, partly as a result of pressure from the host governments and partly because of the need to ensure that all demands for all products can be met in all parts of the world when the outputs of the market located refineries fail to match the product demand. The major implication in this is that the pattern of transport of products will be much less rigid than that for crude oil. The permanence of the large-scale movement of residual oil from the Caribbean to the United States is likely to represent the only important exception to the increasing flexibility in product transport requirements. This trend will be emphasized by the building of refineries in more and more countries, for many of these refineries will throw up surpluses of one or more products which the local market cannot absorb but which have to be produced in order to meet the needs for other products.* Indian refineries, for example, produce surplus gasoline and many of the new African refineries seem likely to have surplus fuel oil to be disposed of. The world pattern of transport of oil products will thus become increasingly more complex and it is this development which provides the international companies with an argument for permitting them, rather than a national concern which might buy its crude supplies somewhat cheaper, to build and operate such

---

* For an international company it is cheaper to provide transport for these surplus products than to invest considerable additional capital in the refinery to eliminate the surplus by reforming or cracking it into a product which is in local demand.

M

refineries. Through their marketing operations in perhaps fifty or more countries, they can invariably find an outlet for any surplus which may be available. A sale to an associated company will, moreover, usually take place at the usual posted price for the product, while a nationalized refinery might often have to accept a distress price owing to the out-of-the-way and qualitatively unknown source from which it is available.

The pattern will be further complicated because many of the new refineries will be minimum cost projects concentrating on producing a narrow range of basic products and hence special products such as aviation fuel, bitumen and lubricants will probably move in increasing quantities from their point of production in the large specialized refineries fed by special crudes particularly appropriate for turning out products of this kind. It seems unlikely, for example, that any of the small refineries in Central America (see pages 133–139) will have facilities for manufacturing either bitumen or lubricating oils. Yet the emphasis on road developments in the plans of these countries for economic development suggests a rapidly increasing demand for bitumen. With better roads, more vehicles may be expected to make use of them and thus increase the demand for lubricating oils. Special imports will thus continue to increase in spite of the development of a local refining industry. In these cases, in fact, the economics of transporting both the crude and the products themselves are rather different from those which affect the industry as a whole. The limited quantities of special crudes needed for their production cannot travel in large tankers and therefore cannot get the benefit of the specially low freight rates that are available for such tankers. The products, on the other hand, have a high unit value and are required in relatively small quantities. They can, therefore, more easily stand higher transport costs from a refinery located at the source of the crude. For example, a unit to provide 100,000 tons of lubricants a year is being added to Texaco's export refinery in Trinidad. A suitable crude is locally obtainable and the lubricants will be transported to many different markets in both the western hemisphere and Western Europe.

A development in product transport which is increasing in importance is the movement of liquified petroleum gases from the main oil producing areas.   The demand for L.P.G. has hitherto been met from the propane and butane produced in the refining processes, but with a rapidly increasing consumption (from only 500,000 tons in 1938 to 19 million tons in 1956 and 25 million tons in 1960) for a variety of purposes, steps are being taken to extract the gases from the wet natural gas produced in association with oil production.   Such extraction has of course to take place at the point of production whereas the main demand lies in the industrial areas of Western Europe and Japan.   In the past, small shipments of propane and butane have been made in pressure tanks (shipped on dry cargo ships or inside the oil tanks of oil tankers) and rather larger amounts have more recently been transported in specialized gas tankers which have not, however, exceeded 7000 tons. The substitution of refrigerated for pressurized storage now offers prospects for cheaper ocean transport, and a ship carrying over 15,000 tons of refrigerated liquified petroleum gases is already operating between Kuwait and Japan.   Special facilities to make refrigerated L.P.G. available for bulk shipment have already been brought on stream in both Kuwait and Saudi Arabia, and further developments in both the Middle East and other producing areas such as Algeria and Venezuela seem to be certain.[3]

The final aspect of the transport of oil is the movement of products from refinery, ocean import terminal or, less frequently, pipeline import terminal through to the tanks of the consumer or the retailer.   In many parts of the world the means of transport is quite simply determined by the limited facilities which happen to be available.   Throughout most of Central America, for example, communications between the import terminals or coastal refineries and the interior are limited to a single railway with perhaps the alternative of a road which may not, however, be passable at all seasons.   Thus, in Guatemala there are single routes from both the Atlantic and the Pacific coasts into the interior highland zone where the bulk of the population lives, including the 380,000 inhabitants of the capital, Guatemala City.   For companies with product supplies available on both coasts, the only question to resolve is where to draw the division between areas served from Puerto Barrios and those from San José (see Figure 17).   As

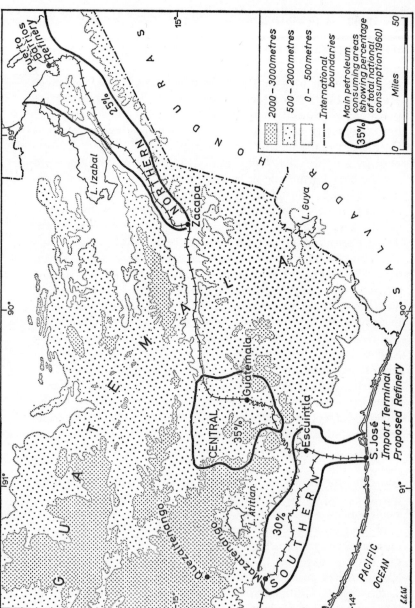

Figure 17. The Distribution of Petroleum Products in Guatemala

supplies from both points will be available at the same price (the import parity price as determined by the international companies) the only consideration is the minimization of distribution costs. Such costs will be related not only to the prices charged for hauling the products but also to the amount of capital needed to establish depots. This latter factor is indeed of great significance in an area, such as the interior of Guatemala, where the demand for products is extensive rather than intensive. The throughput would not justify the construction of more than one major interior installation and the only possible location for it is in Guatemala City which can be fed from both coasts even though it is more than two-thirds of the distance across the country from the Caribbean. Local distribution in Guatemala will thus be based on three points only—the two ocean terminals and the Guatemala City depot— even though from the latter some backhaul of products will be necessary particularly in the direction of the Caribbean coast.

A recent development in West Africa clearly brings out the problems involved in distributing products in areas where the lines of communication are somewhat tenuous. Supplies for Bamako, the capital of Mali, had traditionally been shipped via the railway from Dakar in Senegal. When this link was broken in 1961 as a result of political differences between these two newly independent states, there were only two unstisfactory alternative routes available. The first, and shorter, route was from Conakry in Guinea by railway to Kurussa and then by boat down the Niger (see Figure 18). Two difficulties faced the companies operating in Mali if this route were to be used. The Niger in this stretch is navigable for only about half the year and use of the route would therefore have meant the construction of additional storage capacity at Bamako to ensure regular supplies throughout the year.

Probably more significant than this physical problem was a political difficulty in accepting supplies through Guinea. The companies operating in Mali had run into trouble with the left-wing Guinean government, which was following a policy within the terms of which the companies found it embarrassing to operate. In fact, they had been forced to market supplies of Soviet products accepted by Guinea as part of a bi-lateral trading agreement with the U.S.S.R., and the outlet for their

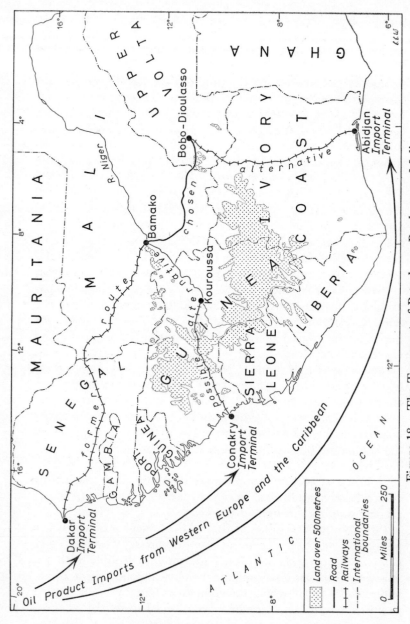

Figure 18. The Transport of Petroleum Products to Mali

own products had thus been severely reduced.   The companies now feared that to take in Mali's supplies through Guinea would invite Soviet intervention in the oil business in a second West African country.   This was particularly important as Mali was experiencing difficulty in finding the necessary foreign exchange for its oil imports and might, therefore, welcome an offer of supplies from the Soviet Union which would certainly accept local products rather than require foreign exchange in return.

The shortest alternative route was thus unacceptable and the companies had to turn to the much longer route: rail transport from Abidjan in the Ivory coast to Bobo Diulasso in High Volta and then motor transport over more than 350 miles of difficult roads to Bamako.   In cases such as these—and difficulties of transport are general throughout much of the developing world—the problem of distributing products is essentially a physical one with little point in worrying unduly about the cost of completing the operation.   Attempts, however, are made to minimize distribution costs even in such areas—sometimes with an apparent willingness to incur a heavy capital outlay in order to achieve it.

In Costa Rica, for example, the companies submitting proposals to the government for refinery construction were faced with the situation that most of the market for the products was in the Meseta Central—the interior highland basin of the country within which 70 per cent. of the population are crowded and where most of the commercial activities requiring an input of energy are concentrated.   They also faced the prospect of high transport charges from the railways which provide the only effective means of getting the products from the ports of Limón on the Caribbean coast and Puntarenas on the Pacific.   To reduce these costs, one company proposed to construct its refinery at Alajuela near the capital, San José, in the centre of the Meseta Central and to lay a sixty-mile crude pipeline from Puntarenas.   Another company proposed to locate its refinery at Puerto Limón and offered to build an all-weather road from the refinery to the capital so as to ensure an element of competition with the railway for the movement of products.

In those parts of the world where transport facilities are

adequate and where the intensity of demand is such as to make a country-wide system of depots a practical proposition, the final stages in the transport of oil are costly in relation to the larger scale movements of crude and products at earlier stages of the process, and hence must be organized to keep costs to an absolute minimum. This process may be demonstrated by reference to the United Kingdom, though it should be borne in mind that in this country the degree of competition permitted between different forms of transport is perhaps greater than in most other industrial nations. Successive governments, in the period since the ending of national control over petroleum distribution in 1950, have not seen fit to offer any degree of protection to the state-owned railways such as is given in many other countries. In both South Africa and New Zealand, for example, rail transport has a monopoly of long distance traffic.

Since the great extension of refinery capacity in the United Kingdom the pattern of distribution has been mainly based on the refineries, whose location is shown in Figure 7. In addition, however, there are still companies which receive products from overseas refineries and their import terminals occupy a position in the pattern of distribution analogous to that of the refineries, although the refineries, of course, present much larger originating units for the distribution process. This is clearly shown by the fact that whereas Shell-Mex and B.P. Ltd. formerly used fourteen main importing centres it now draws its supplies from the six refineries belonging to the parent companies. Over this period, moreover, the amount of products handled has increased fourfold from about 5 million to over 20 million tons. Regent's petroleum products are currently imported through eight ocean terminals from refineries in Trinidad, the Middle East and other European countries. With the announcement that its parent companies plan to build a refinery large enough to meet its entire demand for products in the United Kingdom, the Regent Company will thus centralize its distribution system on one point in the same way that Esso relied entirely on Fawley until the recent opening of its second United Kingdom refinery at Milford Haven.

The delivery of products from a refinery directly to a

consumer is not an insignificant part of the total distribution
process. This arises because of the relationships between the
locations which, in the past, have been suitable for building
refineries—viz. estuarine locations with the availability of
deep water berths—and the distribution of the main centres
of population and industry, which are the main consuming
areas of petroleum products. The six refineries supplying
Shell-Mex and B.P., for example, are on the Thames estuary,
in South Wales, in Lancashire and on the Forth estuary.
With daily deliveries by road possible within a radius of about
sixty miles,* direct distribution from the refineries can thus
cover most of the major industrial areas in the country. By the
use of rail transport it is possible to extend deliveries direct
from refinery to consumer over an even greater area. Evidence
of this is seen in the delivery of fuel oil to the Corby iron and
steel works directly from the Shell Haven refinery on the
Thames, some 100 miles distant.

Outside the areas that can be served directly from the
refineries—and for companies apart from Shell-Mex and B.P.,
this means most of the country (for even the two refineries of
the second most important marketing company—Esso—are
located, on Southampton Water and at Milford Haven,
eccentrically to the major areas of demand). This involves
the need for secondary storage before delivery to the customer,
retailer or wholesaler.† Mr. C. T. Brunner, the late Managing
Director of Shell-Mex and B.P. Ltd., has described the considerations that determine the establishment of such secondary
storage in the following terms:

'The actual number of storages depends basically on the
relationship between laying down costs, that is the cost of getting
supplies to the storage, the costs of delivery to the customer, the
capital costs of storages and the present and estimated future
volume of trade. In turn, these factors are determined by the
type of transport that can be used, the size and number of
customers and, particularly important in many places today, the

---

* Except in the London area where traffic congestion confines direct delivery
by road to a radius of about forty miles.

† The stage at which ownership passes from the marketing company largely
depends on the product; industrial oils are usually sold directly to the customers'
tank; gasoline sales go through a retailer; and kerosene and other home heating
oils are often sold through wholesalers.

availability of suitable land. The volume and pattern of trade gives an approximate idea of where storages should be sited. As costs of delivery to the customer per ton mile are always higher than laying down costs per ton mile, storages should be placed as near as possible to the biggest centres of trade and normally feed away from the direction of the points which supply them. However, because of the economics of bulk handling, it is not a simple question of providing each fairly large centre of population with its own storage. Building up a distribution network is a matter of continual balancing of alternatives and searching for the lowest cost methods.' [4]

With so many variables thus to be taken into account it is not surprising that a start has been made in the use of computers to assess all the possibilities with a view to establishing an optimum (i.e. minimum cost) distribution pattern. This needs to take into account the use of existing facilities, but for these there is a choice either of writing off the equipment and selling the site or of putting more capital in so that the facilities are made adequate. Other factors such as the possibility of making berths for large coastwise tankers (i.e. 16,000-ton vessels) available on a certain site can also be considered in comparison with the use of sites less convenient for markets but more accessible to the large tankers.

C. T. Brunner [5] went on to suggest that the most important factor determining the number of secondary storages is the economies of scale that can be achieved in laying down the oil. In the United Kingdom such economies of scale are gained by the use of large coastal tankers, which can feed coastal storages at points most accessible to the main centres of demand (excluding those served from the refineries themselves). Thus the main emphasis in distribution from the refineries in the United Kingdom is on the use of water transport. Of the output at the Fawley refinery 93 per cent. leaves by sea; over 85 per cent. of the Shell Haven production is shipped out (including the amount sent by barge up the Thames to the riverside depots of the London area). The new refinery at Milford Haven is inconveniently located to distribute more than a small fraction of its output by road and rail, and the overwhelming proportion moves out by sea from the coastal tanker berth specially constructed for this purpose. An indication that all the major companies have arrived at much the same conclusions is shown by the location of parallel facilities by them at the most suitable sites. Shell-Mex and B.P. Ltd., for example, have an installation on Southampton Water opposite to Esso's refinery. Seven of the eight major companies distributing products in the United Kingdom use installations on the Humber. Mobil Oil has one of its ocean terminals and Esso one of its main coastal depots near to Shell's Stanlow refinery.

The use of water transport is, moreover, not restricted to coastwise shipping, for the main coastal storages are located partly in relation to the use that can be made of inland water-ways. For example, from the Humber installations use is made of both canals and rivers to take products to depots as far inland as Nottingham and Leeds, and from the Avonmouth ocean installation, barges move up the Severn as far as Worcester. The preference for the use of water transport in distribution because of the economies that can thereby be affected is clearly shown by the fact that the Leeds depot of Shell-Mex and B.P. Ltd., which is barely seventy miles away from the Shell refinery at Stanlow, is nevertheless mainly fed with products from the Thames-side refineries—a sea and canal journey of over 250 miles. Similarly, depots in the West Midlands, at Worcester for example, are fed by coastal depots and refineries on the Bristol Channel rather than by overland transport from the rather nearer Stanlow refinery. In these instances we see the impact of cheap water transport on storage location and note the clear preference over bulk overland transport by rail. The advantage over road transport, which is usually used for direct distribution from refineries for distances of up to sixty miles, is shown in the location of a coastal installation at Bowling on the Clyde, fed largely from Stanlow over 250 miles away. This installation is designed to meet demand in the Glasgow area—only thirty to forty miles away from the Grangemouth refinery and thus well within the distance normally served by direct delivery by road tanker.

As a result of these considerations the number of secondary storages has been considerably reduced in recent years. Most of the inland ones are now confined to the Midlands lying more than sixty or seventy miles from the nearest convenient coastal location. It has already been shown that use is made of inland waterways where possible, but rail-bridging services, from refineries to depots in areas which cannot be served by water transport, fed by regularly scheduled trains of up to 600 tons have been developed to minimize the cost of overland transport. Examples of such services are those from the Thames-side refineries to depots such as Royston and Thame on the northern fringes of the London conurbation and to Coventry and Rowley Regis in the heart of the Midlands. There are, moreover, other circumstances in which bulk rail facilities are utilized. Few large customers are able to take delivery of their requirements by tanker or by barge but a much greater number have rail connections. In such cases it might well be more economic to feed in supplies by rail directly from refinery or ocean installation to avoid the cost of double-handling from barge to tank and then from tank to road tanker as would occur if a barge fed depot were used. This applies not only to large individual consumers of oil—for example, steel works and large factories—but also to wholesalers responsible for the last stages in the distribution of kerosene and other home heating oils.

The pattern of distribution of petroleum products in the United Kingdom has, therefore, developed in response to changing factors in both the supply and the demand situation as well as to changing transport technology. Two other aspects need to be mentioned briefly. The concentration of refineries (and even more of refinery capacity) in the southern part of the country may have been noted (see Figure 7). This is in part a reflection of the principle that back-hauls, even relatively short distance ones, should be avoided. Thus a northern location for a refinery was to be avoided as this implied that some of the products would have to travel south, back over the same route taken by the crude in the first place. This situation, however, is passing as demand becomes more intensive in the northern parts of the country with the increasing ability of oil to compete with coal even on the latter's home ground. The prospect for a severe cut-back in Scottish coal output together with the inability of the north-western and much of the north-eastern fields to produce coal at competitive prices will set the stage for the expansion of refinery capacity in these areas and thus obviate the first stage in the national distribution pattern—the relatively long haul by coastal tankers from the refineries in the south to ocean storage in the north—which we have just examined.

Finally, what of the prospects for a system of distribution based on pipelines? With coastally located refineries at or near most of the main centres of demand and with most other areas readily accessible by cheap sea or river/canal transport, the prospects seem to be relatively limited. There have already been developments in pipeline transport for special purposes and for specially compelling reasons. London airport, with a consistently high demand for a limited number of products and situated on the 'wrong' side of London from the point of view of the Thames-side refineries supplying much of the fuel with consequent supply problems arising from traffic congestion, provided an ideal case for pipeline development. The fact that Esso have also built a line to the airport from their Fawley refinery indicates that even without the problem of traffic congestion in the London area, the high and increasing demand which will ensure that the line is used to capacity is in itself sufficient to justify the high initial capital cost involved. There are also other examples in which these conditions prevail. The high capital cost of product lines from the Stanlow refinery to Partington near Manchester can be justified in the light of the constant demand arising from both the consumers in the Greater Manchester area and from the needs of the Partington chemical works. The line from Fawley to a chemical plant near Bristol is also guaranteed capacity use over a long period and, moreover, also gives a saving of 75 per cent. in mileage when compared with the journey by sea. Other special cases of this type may be expected, particularly as legislation has now simplified the procedure for obtaining the necessary rights of way.

The major possible development, however, is for the construction of a trunk products pipeline connecting the Thames with the Mersey so that the Midlands, generally inaccessible by water transport, can be relieved of their dependence on rail and road transport. Two pipelines have, in fact, been projected —one by Trunk Pipelines Ltd. and the other by a consortium of the five major marketing companies. The pipelines proposed seem likely to have a capacity of about 3·0 million tons a year and to provide transport at a cost of about 0·5d. per ton mile over distances of 120 miles. Present rail costs over this distance are 1·5d. per ton mile (with actual charges of under 2d. per ton mile). Thus, the pipeline will be an economic proposition from the point of view of the oil companies concerned for it will give a saving in distribution costs of about a farthing on each gallon transported. However, two points must be borne in mind. Firstly, rail costs are likely to be reduced, as the railways are cut back to provide only those services for which they are best suited and are technically equipped to handle tankers of larger capacity and capable of high-speed running.* Thus, more competitive rail rates could push back the break-even point for this pipeline development. Secondly, with lower rail costs reducing the savings to be expected from pipeline transport to a very low level, it seems possible that a government committed to support the railways and accepting responsibility for the Transport Commission's loss may not permit such a pipeline to be built as it would mean a significant abstraction of potential rail traffic. From a national point of view, it could be argued that the expenditure of £8 million or more on a Thames-Mersey pipeline is illogical given a situation in which there is already more than adequate transport capacity available for as much oil as will need to move to the Midlands from the Thames and the Mersey for at least the next decade. Thus, the savings to the oil companies produced from the use of the pipeline seem likely to be offset by the losses arising from the underutilization of other transport facilities—for example, the newly electrified main line from London to Liverpool—in which many millions of pounds of public money has been invested.

* For example, experimental runs are now being made between Fawley refinery and Birmingham (a distance of almost 150 miles) by 'block' trains of twenty rail tankers each carrying almost 30 tons (equal to up to 9000 gallons) of oil products and completing a round-trip every 24 hours. This development doubles the productivity of the present arrangement with a 48 hour turn-round—itself at a very favourable level compared with the average 6–7 days turn-round time required for tank wagons of much smaller capacity. Further developments along these lines could reduce rail costs very significantly.

REFERENCES

1 P. H. Frankel. 'Oil Supplies during the Suez Crisis.' *Journal of Industrial Economics*. Vol. VI, No. 2, February 1958, p. 95.

2 From a speech by Vice-Admiral Hughes-Hallet, Joint Parliamentary Secretary, Ministry of Transport. Reported in *Daily Telegraph*, 27th October 1961.

3 *Petroleum Press Service*. Refrigerating L.P.G. for Ocean Transport. July 1960, p. 241. Growing Fleet of L.P.G. Tankers. January 1962, p. 14.

4 C. T. Brunner. 'Productivity in Oil Distribution in Britain.' Paper given to the Economics section of the British Association Meeting, Norwich, 1961.

5 C. T. Brunner. *Ibid*.

PART IV

CONCLUSION

CHAPTER 8

The Oil Industry
and Economic Development

The first three parts of this book have attempted to explain the spatial distribution of oil industry activity. An economic geography which seeks to analyze the distribution of one industry would not, however, appear to be complete without some consideration being given to the relationship of that industry to the areas within which its activities are located. A brief examination was made in Part II of the general correlation between economic development and the use of energy—particularly oil. This concluding part, therefore, is concerned specifically with the impact of oil in those countries in which the oil is produced, and whose production forms, in many cases, the main economic activity.

The contrast in the impact of the production of coal and of oil on the development of industrial regions has been stressed in much geographical analysis. For example, Estall and Buchanan in discussing 'Energy Sources and Industrial Location' observed:

> 'Oil does not in general attract major industries to its source of origin . . . major industrial concentrations are not a normal feature of oilfields as they have been of coalfields.' [1]

The past and, to a large degree, the present validity of the point can be accepted. It would seem to depend on the interplay of four separate criteria.

The first arises from the relative ease and cheapness with which oil can be transported compared with coal. Even by sea by bulk carrier, the cost of moving coal is about 0·1d. per ton mile compared with less than 40 per cent. of this for the shipment of an amount of oil containing the same amount of energy.* Coastwise around the United Kingdom, oil is carried at less than 0·5d. per ton mile whereas the cost of moving coal from Northumberland to London is of the order of 0·6d. per ton mile. Thus the coastwise movement of coal is about twice as expensive as that of oil on a calorie basis. Overland transport costs for the two sources of energy on a ton for ton basis are probably not very different for rail and road haulage when equally modern facilities, especially for loading and unloading, are employed, but it must be constantly borne in mind that a ton of oil provides at least one and a half times as much useful energy as a ton of coal and thus a given requirement of energy always necessitates a more limited use of transport for oil than for coal. Moreover, whilst rail and road haulage are often the rule for coal they are almost the exception for oil. In the United States they together account for only 5 per cent. of total crude and product movement and in the United Kingdom supply only about 10 per cent. of transport from the refineries. Given the necessary degree of intensity of demand oil products can be moved by pipeline; this cheaper means of overland transport is still very much in the experimental stage for coal. With such inherent advantages in transport costs, there is obviously less compelling reason with oil than with coal to ensure that consumption takes place as near as possible to the point of production.

Secondly, oil came into use as a fuel much later than coal. The latter provided the main source of fuel and power for almost a century before oil became significant even in the United States, and it still holds the dominating position in much of the rest of the industrialized world. In changing over to the use of oil fuel for, in most cases, relatively small savings in total costs of production or because a better product can thereby be made (for example, for certain grades of steel and for bricks), most enterprises would find no compelling reason for changing the location of their operations, and even expansion of the industry would be more likely to be related

---

* This is based on a comparison of transatlantic rates for United States coal exports with the rates for ocean tankers in 1961. The lower cost of moving energy in the form of oil is partly due to the greater size of oil tankers compared with coal carriers and partly to the fact that two tons of oil provides roughly the same amount of energy as three tons of coal.

to the existence and location of similar producers than to the location of the source of the supplies of oil. Thus, in part at least, the availability of oil has tended to confirm the degree of regional specialization produced by an initial dependence on coal. However, because the use of oil has enabled the input of energy to be reduced in both volumetric and monetary terms, it has also been one of the factors contributing to the dispersionary and market trends in industrial location. With a trend away from coalfield location of industry, a location related to the more easily transported supplies of oil would be somewhat illogical.

Thirdly, the phenomenon may be related to the way in which the oil industry has been organized. As shown in Chapter 2, about 80 per cent. of oil production in the non-communist world outside North America is still controlled by the international oil companies. The percentage has been even higher in the past. The interests of these companies have been mainly in the development of the oil resources of the world at large for sale in the energy hungry economies of North America, Western Europe and Japan. The producing countries have been paid by means of royalties, taxes and in other similar ways, and the companies have had neither need nor incentive to increase the consumption of oil at the point of production by encouraging industry and commerce. In fact, as, under the terms of their concession agreements or because of other government pressures, they have sometimes had to sell their oil more cheaply in the country of production than to the rest of the world they have had a powerful incentive not to encourage the local offtake. This seems to be the position in Venezuela, for example, where the prices charged locally for main products are lower than those posted at the refineries for sale overseas.

The oil companies have, in general, remained oil companies, their profits being either distributed or ploughed back into one aspect or another of the oil business (together with petro-chemicals). They have not put their profits into other enterprises, particularly in the countries where production has been located, for fear of having too many eggs in the same rather precarious basket.

The situation is, however, changing. Just as countries

offering concessions now insist that resource-located refineries shall be constructed once production from a concession reaches a certain level, so they are now seeking other industrial activities to provide a higher degree of employment and a more widely based industrial sector as an insurance against the future depletion of their oil. This development will be examined in more detail later in the chapter. An indication of changing attitudes on the part of the major international companies came with the announcement by Creole Petroleum in Venezuela— the affiliated company of Standard Oil of New Jersey—that it was putting $10 million on one side to invest in Venezuelan non-oil enterprises, preferably in conjunction with local private Venezuelan capital. Creole's suggestions for the type of enterprise in which this capital might be used accord quite closely with the World Bank Mission's recommendation for economic diversification in Venezuela and suggest an appreciation by Jersey of the need to make the country's economy less dependent on oil.* This type of application of capital generated in the oil industry seems to be analogous to the kinds of investment made in branches of local industry by the coal-mining entrepreneurs of nineteenth-century Britain or the United States, which helped to establish the coal-mining regions as industrial centres. It represents a significant break with traditional policy and has not been universally welcomed by the other international oil companies, which may, however, be obliged to follow suit for political reasons and thus provide an additional means for industrial expansion in the oil-producing countries.

Fourthly, oil production has been concentrated, outside the United States, in the under-developed parts of the world, where local conditions have not in general been propitious for industrial development. The absence of capital and of the institutional machinery for raising capital, the lack of suitable labour and in some cases of labour of any description and the absence of basic elements in the social and economic infrastructure of society, coupled with generally unfavourable conditions of climate and location have together precluded the

---

* There were, moreover, reports in 1962 that the first results of this investment showed a better return on capital than that from Creole's oil investment in Venezuela!

formation of complex industrially advanced regions.   Indeed, such conditions preclude even the organization of an effective agriculture capable of providing the foodstuffs for the personnel engaged in oil operations.   For example, the requirements of oil industry personnel in Venezuela for horticultural products, dairy products and many other items of food have been met by importing these things from North America or Western Europe.   The relevance of these factors is brought out by S. H. Longrigg in his descriptions of the problems attendant upon the production of oil in Qatar.   In his book, *Oil in the Middle East*,[2] he speaks of 'the flat and arid peninsula of Qatar, with scarcely more permanent settlement than its village capital, Dohra, no cultivation, and almost no vegetation, no water drinkable by Europeans and a population of a few thousand starveling tribesmen and fisherfolk.'   He goes on to describe the territory as 'totally devoid of resources with Qatari's labour wholly unskilled and weak through malnutrition.'   Later in the book he shows that the importing of workers from outside— clerks from India and Pakistan, artisans from Jordan, Palestine and Iraq and labourers from Dhofar and elsewhere in Arabia— was indispensable in spite of 'all possible efforts to give pride of place to Qataris.'   In such a situation the successful initiation of oil producing operations was obviously as far as industrialization and economic development could hope to go for a considerable time: there was no basis whatsoever for other forms of industrial enterprise.

Having thus established four different sets of factors which have led to contrasts between coalfields and oilfields as seats of other significant economic activity, we may note that while the first is inherent in the physical differences between oil and coal and the second the result of the impact of the historical development of the western economies, the third is but a temporary phenomenon relevant only to one period of development of the industry and the fourth does not have universal applicability. Because the third and fourth set of factors do not reinforce the first and second in all regions of the world, it would seem to be unsatisfactory to view the contrast in the impact of coal and of oil on the development of industrial regions in terms of a principle.   There are, in fact, already industrial complexes based on the local production of oil, and it seems possible that the latter part of the twentieth century will see a further significant development of the phenomenon.

Industrial complexes based on the production of oil have, perhaps, to date depended to a large degree on the additional local availability of natural gas from an oilfield and the growing use of both oil and gas as the most important basic raw material for the chemical industry. The significance of the use of natural gas in this respect should not be under-estimated, for it is partly the result of the oil industry's earlier inability to use, or to make available for use, this resource that oilfield-oriented industrial development has been so slow to develop. The illogicality of the situation whereby natural gas was treated merely as a by-product of oil production is clearly brought out by W. E. Pratt, a former Vice-President of the Standard Oil Company of New Jersey in charge of exploration. He wrote:

> 'Oil fields are essentially gas fields; oil in the earth is more gas than oil. . . . While we search for oilfields and record our discoveries in terms of barrels of oil, what we really find is gas, with which is associated a subordinate quantity of oil.'[3]

The gas has been less attractive to seek and to utilize because it cannot be adapted to many of the uses to which oil is put (for example, in transport) and because it is less readily stored and transported at low cost and without waste.

Thus, in the Middle East, Venezuela and the Sahara the natural gas equivalent of about 45 million tons of coal was flared off in 1961 and an even greater amount probably used to repressure the oilfields of these areas. For example, in Saudi Arabia of a total gas production of 718 million cubic feet daily (equivalent to about 10 million tons of coal a year), only 50 million—about 7 per cent.—were used as fuel while 402 million were reinjected into the oilwells and 265 million were flared off. In Iran production was 635 million cubic feet daily; 75 million were used for fuel and the remainder burned to no useful purpose. In Venezuela 49 per cent. of the production of 3045 million cubic feet daily was wasted—the equivalent of almost 15 per cent. of the coal production of Britain.

The unlikelihood of ever shipping more than a small

percentage of the gas available, in spite of the successful experiments with refrigerated ocean tankers, and the unwillingness of the producing countries to continue to see one of their major natural resources wasted, has led to proposals for the development of industries to consume the gas. At the Arab Oil Congress in Alexandria in 1961, Sheik Abdullah Tariki, then the Saudi Arabian Minister of Mines and Mineral Resources, indicated that his government would seek to encourage the establishment of energy consuming enterprises such as electricity generation, petrochemicals and the distillation of sea water.[4] In Kuwait a petrochemical company was formed in 1960 with the object of using natural gas to manufacture urea, polyvinylchloride, caustic soda and other products. In Venezuela, the World Bank Mission has recommended the expansion of the chemical industry to make use of the available natural gas and suggested that a market survey be carried out to assess what new outlets can be secured.[5] Though such developments may be slow to be achieved, they seem certain to become of increasing significance as both capital for the projects and markets for the products become available. Their failure to develop will reflect not the nature and attributes of oil and gas as such but rather the over-riding handicaps to the economic, and particularly the industrial, development of the under-developed countries in competition with the older established industrial centres of the world.[6]

This problem has not, of course, hindered the development of an important industrial complex along the Gulf Coast of the United. States based on the local production and refining of oil and the associated production and use of natural gas in the chemical and other industries. Although the distribution of natural gas throughout the United States has been made possible by the development of an extensive network of pipelines, local use of the gas is encouraged by the relatively high costs of transport. Thus, while the well-head price of gas in Texas and Oklahoma is, on an average, only 10 cents per 1000 cubic feet, the average price to consumers in Illinois, some 600 miles away, amounts to 37·9 cents for industrial use, 56·8 cents for commercial use and up to 110·7 cents for residential use. The advantages to be gained from locating the chemical industry—using natural gas both as a fuel and as raw material—at the point of production on the oilfields rather than elsewhere in the United States is readily apparent. There are already over 100 major petrochemical plants located in the region, with more than half the country's new plants and extensions of plants announced for the area.[7]

The development of an industrial complex of this kind in which the basic industry's use of land, of capital and to a less degree of labour, and which gradually but inevitably attracts a range of secondary and tertiary economic activities seems to present a phenomenon of the same order of magnitude as the traditional iron and steel complexes of the nineteenth century. This development is perhaps at the moment unique, but there are indications that other examples will develop in countries which produce oil and natural gas largely for their own consumption, which depend on these fuels for the major part of their energy requirements and which can consume domestically the major part of their industrial production and therefore do not have to worry unduly about competition in potential export markets from the major industrial regions. In these countries industry has not already developed at locations based on the supply of coal and there is not the problem that countries such as Kuwait and Saudi Arabia are likely to meet of marketing the chemicals and other products abroad. Mexico seems to offer the most immediate possibilities. The ambitious petrochemical programme announced in 1961 by Pemex, the state oil company, is to be based largely on developments in the oil-producing areas of the country, all of which are located along the Gulf Coast. For example, a petrochemical complex to produce tetraethyl lead, acetaldehyde, vinyl chloride, soda ash, bromine, chlorine and ethylene derivatives is to be built at the port of Coatzacoalas in the centre of the southern and principal oil and gas producing area. Somewhat less definitely, there are also prospects for the establishment of a petrochemical complex in the oil and gas fields of the Argentine province of Patagonia. Here the government is to offer special incentives, including tax relief and exemptions from customs duties, to firms establishing or expanding their plants in this area. Following the successful development of a petrochemical industry, the government feels that there will then be the basis for other types of industrial and commercial activity, with the desirable end result of establishing a new region of economic significance at one of the extremities of the country so as to provide a more effective balance against the dominance of the Buenos Aires area.

In the main, therefore, industrial development associated with oil and gas is based in the first instance on their uses as raw materials in the rapidly expanding chemical industry. This is seen in developments at Lacq in the centre of the main oil and gas field in south-west France, where sulphur, basic chemicals, fertilizers and plastics are being produced in rapidly increasing quantities.

It would, however, be incorrect to dismiss entirely the possibilities of developing even the traditional industrial complex of iron and steel on the basis of local availability of oil and gas.   The development of the processes in which fuel oil or natural gas can be injected into blast furnaces, partly eliminating the need for coke, may encourage the development of the iron and steel industry either on the oil and gas fields themselves or on ore fields conveniently located for supplies of oil and gas.   One would not consider this likely in a country such as the United States, within which the major steel pro- ducing areas are already located with reference to the existing relevant production and transport costs.   Economic inertia alone would probably inhibit such a change in location.   In those countries, however, where the iron and steel industry is not developed but in which its development is considered essential for various political and economic reasons, such development will be greatly encouraged by the availability of oil and gas, particularly when, as in many countries of this kind, supplies of coal are either not available domestically or are of unsatisfactory quality; and it would seem logical to exploit first those ore bodies which are in close relationship with these newer fuels.   Thus, the under-developed countries which also happen to be important oil producers could secure an advantage over other under-developed countries in the general effort to achieve self-sufficiency in, and exports of, steel.   Incidentally, in addition to providing a means whereby the costs of steel production can be reduced, the oil industry gives another advantage in that its demands for steel products of many kinds, but especially for steel tubes, provide a ready market for the industry. Partly for these reasons, one could suggest that the plans for steel industries in Iran, Venezuela and Argentina stand rather more chance of coming to fruition than those of many other countries.

The relationships between oil producing areas and major industrial developments are not, however, the only relevant considerations when examining the impact of the oil industry on the economic geography of a country. There are also other significant direct physical effects arising from the producing and resource-located refining operations of the oil industry.

In the first place, the significance of the oil industry itself in modifying the landscape should not be forgotten. Though exploration and 'wildcatting' produce changes of a transient character only (for example, the development of impermanent settlements and a temporary and fluctuating demand for a limited amount of local labour), the development of an oilfield produces changes in the landscape of a permanent nature, for an oil company must be convinced of the long-term prospects of a field before committing itself to the very large-scale capital expenditure needed for the production of the oil. In Venezuela, the Bolivar field on the eastern shore of Lake Maracaibo has been producing oil since 1918. The impact of this has been described in the following terms by Preston-James:[8]

'Oil derricks along the swampy shore and in the lake itself are a part of an intricate pattern of pipelines, pumping stations, storage tanks, and company offices. . . . Perhaps the greatest transformation of all has been accomplished within the city of Maracaibo. In 1918 this was a small primitive town of some 15,000 inhabitants, mostly Indian and Negro. Its aspect had changed little since the 18th century. . . . In the short span of ten years it became the second city in Venezuela, a little metropolis with paved streets, modern public services, tall office buildings, golf clubs and substantial dwellings. Its population is about 150,000 * of whom at least 30,000 are white foreigners.'

Thus investment in oil operations with its accompanying requirements for labour and the consequent demand for goods and services has transformed a climatically oppressive region, formerly largely dependent upon subsistence agriculture, fishing and the provision of transport on the rivers and across

* Maracaibo's population is now over 250,000.

the lake into an area supporting a population as dense as that in any other part of the country.[9] To the north of Lake Maracaibo, the Paraguana peninsula was very sparsely inhabited, as the absence of reliable rainfall made agriculture virtually impossible. The establishment on the peninsula of two of the largest oil refineries in the world—in order to comply with the insistence of the Venezuelan government in 1943 that a greater percentage of Venezuelan oil should be refined at home—has provided a new basis for economic activity on the peninsula, which in 1950 had a population of 12,300 compared with only 2700 in 1936.

In the Middle East there are many examples of the direct impact of oil activities on the landscape. Drilling in Bahrain began in 1931 and within a few months an important find was made which led the Bahrain Petroleum Company to invest capital in development wells and in storage installations and a terminal. By 1938 the oil industry in Bahrain—an island previously largely dependent on the pearl trade, which had been depressed for many years—was providing employment for over 3000 people (including more than 2000 Bahrainis) and had led to the growth of a completely new town, 'Awali. A refinery was started in 1937 and its capacity doubled during the war, when a drum manufacturing and filling plant was also built. New tankage, pipelines, services, amenities and housing had to be provided for the increased activity and for the additional personnel involved. The number of Bahrainis employed increased to 6000 with an additional employment of almost 3000 foreigners. Post-war developments in both production (which has increased to about 2·5 million tons per annum from over 100 wells) and in refining and associated exporting facilities have further enhanced the transformation of Bahrain, whose population has increased from about 80,000 in 1931 * to over 142,000 in 1960.[10]

In Iran the initial discovery of oil in 1908 was made at Masjid-i-Sulaiman in an area described by S. H. Longrigg as 'a broken and uncultivable waste, with a climate of extreme severity and totally devoid of all resources'.[11] Development quickly followed the discovery and by 1914, by which time about thirty wells had been sunk, 'the first beginnings of

* The first census in 1941 showed a total population of 89,970.

permanent housing, amenities and a settled social life were
made at the oilfield; dry stream beds were made passable,
a water supply provided, gathering lines and tankage erected,
workshops and stores organised, and a club and a hospital
appeared'.[12]   On the coast, the company secured a site on
Abadan Island ('an uninhabited mudflat') for the construction
of a refinery.   The transformation of significant areas of Iran
as a result of producing, transporting and refining activities
of the Anglo-Persian Oil Company was under way.   The
discovery of five more oilfields and a gas field in this under-
developed south-western part of Iran necessitated the development of settlements in which the 20,000 field workers and their
families could live and in which the services such as electric
power stations, stores and workshops were located.   Roads
had to be built both within the fields and to provide a means
of linking them together.   The population of the small town
of Ahwaz, on the navigable river Karun and on the trans-
Persian railway from Bandar Shahpur to Teheran, expanded
from 15,000 in 1900, to 35,000 in 1910 and to about 100,000
in 1960 as the result of its proximity to the northern oilfields
and its functions as the pipeline headquarters for the four most
northerly fields, the transfer point from river and railway
transport from the coast to road transport into the fields and a
main station for stores and workshops.[13]

The main direct impact of the oil industry in Iran, however,
has not been in the producing areas but on Abadan Island,
formerly occupied by only a few fishermen and date growers.
By 1945 its population stood at 120,000 and it now exceeds
300,000,[14] most of whom are dependent directly or indirectly
on the refinery and associated oil activities.   A survey made
in 1959 [15] showed that of the total *active* population of 51,000,
about 27,000 were employed in the refinery and another
17,000 in activities (commerce, services, transport) dependent
in large part on the refinery.   Thus, almost 90 per cent. of
total employment is connected with the oil industry, making
Abadan very much a one industry town.   Although employment provided by the refinery has not grown during the last
ten years, the population has continued to increase because
of a continual inflow of people attracted from the poorer areas
of Iran by rumours of jobs and as a result of the high birth rate

and low death rate resulting from improved sanitation and medical facilities.[16] The result is of course poverty, over-crowding and severe unemployment estimated at about 20 per cent. of the working population.[17] The oil industry, having called into being an urban agglomeration, now faces the serious geographical problem—with its physical, social, economic and political aspects—of making the Abadan area into a viable unit. The task is made doubly difficult by the fact that the refinery is grossly overstaffed by modern standards (it employs eight times as many men per unit of output as the average in Venezuela). There seem to be few hopes of any further large-scale expansion in oil industry activity because of the unlikelihood of the refinery regaining its former impor-tance (the throughput of 25 million tons in 1950 was a peak figure and may be compared with a throughput of about 18 million tons in 1961) in the face of the growth of refinery capacity in almost all consuming countries. More than two-thirds of Iran's oil production is now exported as crude oil directly from the terminals at Mashur and Kharg Island, which are much more conveniently located for the expanding output of the Aghi Jari and Gach Saran oilfields.

A second aspect of the direct physical effect of oil industry operations arises from the usefulness of projects, which are undertaken in the search for and the development of oil resources, in other sectors of a country's economy, with a beneficial impact on the local expansion of activities. This is perhaps most apparent in the development of communications. In western Canada, for example, many hundreds of miles of roads have been laid down by companies looking for or developing oil resources, and they are of course available for general use. The opening up of northern Alberta to many forms of economic activity has been made possible by the availability of landing strips built by the oil companies to gain access to remote leases. In Venezuela, Lake Maracaibo has been opened to ocean-going shipping since the oil industry financed the dredging of a deep-water channel through the sand bars at the entrance. In eastern Venezuela parts of the *llanos* have been made available for possible exploitation by the construction of a network of roads and airstrips by com-panies seeking petroleum.[18] In the Middle East, the entrance to the Shatt al Arab, the channel by which the Iraqi port of Basra is reached, was dredged by means of a loan from the Anglo-Iranian oil company, which was anxious to provide easier access to Abadan. The development is of course of permanent value to the port of Basra, whose efficient operation is made possible to a large extent by virtue of the dues paid to it by the 1000 or more tankers which use the waterway each year. In Saudi Arabia, the sole concessionary company, Aramco, constructed a harbour with fully equipped wharves at Damman and from there built a 355-mile standard gauge railway serving the major oilfields of Abqaiq and Ghawar on its route to the formerly isolated capital of Riyadh.

The impact on water supplies has also been significant. Drilling for oil in arid regions has often made available for general use previously unknown supplies of underground water. Such developments have taken place in Saudi Arabia where, for example, at Kharj, about fifty miles from Riyadh, not only were wells sunk and the water supplies discovered and made available but in addition an agricultural project was developed which involved the installation of pumping plant, the digging of canals and the levelling and bringing into cultivation of some 20,000 acres of land.[19] In Kuwait, earlier failures to find anything but brackish water unsuitable for human consumption, have recently been redeemed by the discovery of sweet water in the northern part of the country, where drilling for oil started in 1955. In the Sahara, the longstanding belief that underground water existed in large quantities has recently been justified with the development of water supplies from wells sunk for oil and gas. For example, in 1959 water was 'struck' at a depth of 5500 feet in a well near Touggourt and flowed at a rate of almost 5000 gallons a minute. These additional supplies of water have revived the existing palm plantations, have enabled another 750 acres of plantation to be established and have made possible the irrigation of 500 acres of market gardens.[20]

A final aspect of the direct effect of oil operations can be seen in the growth of ancillary and contracting services in producing and refining areas. This of course has an impact on the total population and on the settlement pattern. In Alberta, the major producing province of Canada, only

25,000 workers—about 6 per cent. of the total labour force—
are directly employed in producing, refining and transporting
oil.   Oil operations, however, have also given an important
stimulus to employment in the construction industry, in services
and in the retail and wholesale trades.   The construction
industry increased its employment by 250 per cent. in ten years,
thousands of workers were added to wholesale and retail trades
to supply the oil industry with machinery, equipment and
materials and the service industries boomed as jobs and
population expanded.   From 1930 to 1947 (except for a
temporary respite during the war) the population of Alberta
declined with the contraction of agricultural employment,
which provided over 40 per cent. of total employment opportunities in 1946, and in the numbers employed in coal mining.
Since 1947—the date of the major Leduc discovery, which led
to Alberta's becoming one of the world's major oil producing
areas—the population increased by 40 per cent. in ten years in
spite of continued adverse conditions in the agricultural sector
of its economy.   This is largely the result of oil industry
development, as is the increase in the urban population of the
province in this period.[21]

The aspects of the impact of oil on economic development so
far considered in this chapter form, however, only one of the
two sides of the total picture.   The other side arises from the
indirect impact of the payments of royalties, taxes and other
levies by the companies which secure and work concessions in
the oil-rich countries.   The payments are available to finance
the foreign exchange needs of development schemes which can
thus be undertaken on a much broader basis with a lesser
danger of inflation and adverse effects on the country's balance
of payments.*   The application of this capital involves changes
in the type, direction and rate of economic development,
producing changes in the landscape which can thus be indirectly
attributed to oil industry activities.

In most of the major oil producing countries outside North

* The rest of the discussion on this matter will appear to indicate that there is a
direct relationship between the availability of finance from oil industry payments
and the possibilities for development projects.   In fact, as the two preceding
sentences suggest, the relationship is a much more complex economic one.   Here
however, we are concerned with the impact of oil industry payments on the
geography of the oil-producing countries and the author hopes that, in the light
of this objective, the over-simplification of the economic process will be acceptable.

America, such payments by the oil companies are made to the central government and the capital is thus available on a national basis rather than for projects located within the areas of oil industry development.* Two developments have led to a rapid increase in the importance of this source of development finance in the period since 1945. The first has been the great increase in the off-take of oil from the main producing countries, as payments have in this period been related to the amount of oil produced. The second has been the success of the governments of the producing countries in increasing their share of the profits made on each barrel of oil produced.

In Venezuela, for example, the petroleum companies 'enjoyed almost complete freedom of action until 1933',[22] with their financial obligations to the country limited to what was needed to keep the dictator, Gomez, favourable to their activities. Until 1942 only about 20 per cent. of the profits went to the state, but the percentage increased to '25 per cent. in 1942, 35 per cent. in 1944, 50 per cent. in 1946 and 60 per cent. in 1958'.[23] Later negotiations between the government and the oil companies have increased the Venezuelan share of the industry's profits to almost 70 per cent. In the Middle East, pre-war payments to governments were relatively low but in 1950 the principle of a 50 : 50 division of profits was accepted by Aramco in Saudi Arabia.[24] The principle was extended over the next few years to all other concessions in the Middle East, and in recent years additional payments have had to be offered by companies anxious to secure concessions in the face of many competitors. In 1960, for example, no fewer than eight companies applied for the Kuwait off-shore concession. There were offers from four United States 'independent' companies (or groups of companies), from a Japanese group, from the Italian state company, E.N.I., from the Shell Group and from a consortium of three of the other major international companies. All offered terms which would have given Kuwait much more than the traditional 50 : 50 division of profits. In fact, the Kuwait government estimated that for two of the bids it would have received 78·9 per cent.

* It should be noted, however, that in countries with a federal type of constitution the payments are often divided between the central government and the government of the state in which the oil activities are located. This is so in Nigeria and India, for example.

of the actual total net profit expected on the basis of production costs of 40 cents a barrel and a realized price of $1.35 cents per barrel (with a posted price of $1.50).[25] The concession, however, was awarded to the Shell Group which, while appearing to tender on the basis of the conventional 50 : 50 division of profits, offered, as additional incentives, initial and production bonuses totalling £30 million plus annual rentals, as well as agreeing to a 20 per cent. Kuwaiti capital participation in the enterprise, when and if oil is discovered, and to future co-operation with the Kuwait government in the provision of tanker transport and in other sectors of the industry.

The following table shows the oil revenues accruing each year from 1950 to 1960 to the principal oil producing countries.

TABLE 13

STATE REVENUES
DERIVED FROM OIL INDUSTRY ACTIVITIES, 1950–60

(in millions of United States dollars)

Year	Venezuela	Saudi Arabia	Iran	Iraq	Kuwait	Qatar	Total
1950	370	113	45	15	12	1	556
1951	415	165	23	39	18	4	664
1952	426	212	0*	112	57	10	817
1953	475	226	0*	144	169	18	1032
1954	445	281	9	191	194	30	1150
1955	512	275	91	206	282	35	1401
1956	971†	283	153	193‡	293	36	1929
1957	1141†	303	213	144‡	308	45	2154
1958	1030	302	272†	237	354	61	2256
1959	951	315	258	252	409	53	2238
1960	906	332	285	267	409	62	2261

* Revenues ceased following nationalization crisis.
† Includes sales of concessions.
‡ Revenues reduced by damage to pipelines to Mediterranean.

Sources: U.N. Economic Developments in the Middle East 1959–61. Shell International Petroleum Company. *The Economic Impact of Oil Operations in Producing Countries* 1959.

Thus, during the last decade the oil revenues of the major oil exporting countries have increased by about four times, so that even after making allowance for the rise in the price of imports in this period, these countries have enjoyed a considerable real increase in their incomes from this source.

In Venezuela, during the last decade, the revenue derived from the petroleum industry has accounted for about 60 per cent. of the total revenue of the government, which has consequently had finance available for important development projects, although owing to the excesses of dictatorial rulers 'the extent to which government revenues from oil have been utilized to promote the economic welfare of the people leaves much to be desired'.[26] The deliberate use of petroleum revenue to bring about the modernization and diversification of the economy dates from the late 1930s, when the slogan 'Sembrar el petróleo' (sowing the petroleum) was adapted and a three-year programme of development was initiated. The programme included 'railway, schools, hospitals, sewer systems and waterworks, the encouragement of immigration and tourism and the promotion of domestic agriculture and industry'.[27] At best as events turned out, however, little more than a beginning was made to laying down long-term plans for future developments.

A more determined effort to use the revenue from petroleum came about in 1945 when the October revolution overthrew the last of a series of dictators and for the first time brought to power a party (Acción Democrática) which represented the people.[28] With an ideological belief in the need for government direction of the economy, it established the Venezuelan Development Corporation (V.D.C.) as the central planning body for 'sowing the petroleum'. Of the government's annual income, 5 per cent.—that is, about 10 per cent. of petroleum revenues—were set aside to finance developments in agriculture and industry. Between 1945 and 1948 loans were made to expand food production, to resurrect the livestock industry, to promote schemes for mechanization and irrigation and to finance a scheme of land reform. On the industrial side credits were extended to plants designed to produce goods normally imported and the Corporation initiated projects for the expansion of electricity output and the development of a steel industry. Industrial production almost doubled in this period.

The overthrow of the government in 1948 by a new military dictatorship—under Peréz Jimínez—did not bring to an end the policy of using the revenue from petroleum for economic development, but it did alter its aim. Instead of the revenue being used for the balanced development of the economy, it was now used on a limited number of expensive and eye-catching projects. Thus, the plans for agricultural development were largely abandoned and industry in general was not encouraged. From 1948 to 1958 the increasing revenues from oil, including the bonuses amounting to almost $1000 million from the sales of concessions in 1956 and 1957, were devoted to military expenditure, to a limited number of grandiose projects in Caracas, whose population trebled in this period to 1·1 million, and to spectacular constructions such as the motorway from Caracas to La Guaira and the huge irrigation/hydro-electricity dam in Guarico.

Jimínez was overthrown in 1958 and a government under R. Betancourt, the leader of the Acción Democrática, was elected to office. In 1960 it drew up a four-year development programme to be financed from oil revenue which the government expected would increase by about 5 per cent. per annum. The expenditure involved under the plan was to exceed £2500 million but, as a result of doubt concerning the practicability of such a programme in the light of increasing difficulties in marketing Venezuelan oil, against the competition of cheaper supplies from other countries and the partial closure of the main outlet in the United States, the World Bank was asked for advice. Its report and recommendations, published in 1961,[29] clearly brought out the outstanding degree of dependence of the schemes for economic development on the success of the oil industry in expanding its production and sales. A lesser degree of optimism concerning the future prospects for oil (the prospects for increasing revenues were estimated at about 3·5 per cent. per annum) led the World Bank to advocate a less ambitious programme of economic development. However, in that the programme envisages the expenditure shown in Table 14, and recommends the continuation of major schemes of land resettlement, an expanding metallurgical industry in the Guayana region and the development of agricultural activities in areas of the country which at the moment are hardly used, the impact of its implementation on Venezuelan geography will still be considerable.

TABLE 14

ECONOMIC AND SOCIAL DEVELOPMENT IN VENEZUELA

Annual Average Expenditure Recommended by the World Bank Mission for the period, 1961–64

		Millions of bolivares*	Percentage
(a)	*Basic Economic Overheads*	*535*	*28·2*
	of which: Transport	428	22·5
	Power	64	3·4
	Telecommunications	43	2·3
(b)	*Agriculture*	*378*	*19·9*
	of which: Credit Programmes	138	7·3
	Irrigation and Drainage	74	3·9
	Settlement	100	5·3
(c)	*Industry*	*343*	*18·1*
	of which: Credit Programmes	110	5·9
	Steel	200	10·5
	Chemicals	33	1·7
(d)	*Education, Health and Social Services*	*447*	*23·5*
	of which: Education	104	5·5
	Housing	140	7·4
	Water and Sewage	115	6·0
	Hospitals and Health Centres	26	1·4
	Community Development	62	3·2
	Total Annual Expenditure	1900	

* The official rate of exchange is approximately 9.4 bolivares to the £

Source: International Bank for Reconstruction and Development, *The Economic Development of Venezuela*, 1961, p. 38.

In the Middle East, the more recent growth of oil revenues (see Table 13) has produced a crop of development programmes designed to put the available money towards longer-term economic expansion. As in Venezuela, far too much of the oil revenues have previously been wasted. In Saudi Arabia, for example, of the $212 million paid to the government in 1952, no less than 25 per cent. 'was absorbed by the town and royal settlement of Riyadh, the capital', including the claims of the royal family, the cost of administration and the payment of 'doles and presents to tribes and irregulars'.[30]

Iraq and Iran have both instituted development programmes to administer significant percentages of total oil revenues. In Iraq the cornerstone of the development plan—initiated in 1951—has been appropriations for flood control, drainage and irrigation, to which was allocated about 30 per cent. of the total credits available. The projects are designed to harness the waters of the Tigris and the Euphrates and thereby to expand the area and the fertility of the cultivated land of Iraq. With the completion of four major projects—the Samarra and Ramadi barrages and the dams at Dokan and Darbandi-i-Khan in the mountains of north-east Iraq—it is hoped to irrigate an additional 4 million acres of land. This scheme, together with others for the adoption of new agricultural techniques and crop improvements provides the opportunity progressively to transform Iraqi agriculture and to improve living standards for the 80 per cent. of the population who remain dependent on the land.

Other capital in the development plan is allocated to railway modernization, to a new port at Umm Qasr, to extensive road development and to the expansion of industry and mining designed to provide additional employment opportunities.

The success of the plan will inevitably depend upon the continued and increasing flow of revenue from oil industry activities. The possibility that the revenues will not be available as required is, however, very real unless a *modus vivendi* can be achieved between the government and the Iraq Petroleum Company, which until 1962 held almost the entire country under concession. Failure to reach an agreement would seem to imply reducing revenues as the oil companies which form the I.P.C. reduce their off-take of Iraqi oil and obtain their requirements from other countries.

In Iran the large-scale availability of oil revenue was delayed until 1955 as a result of the virtual cessation of oil activities during the dispute between the Mossadeq government and the Anglo-Iranian oil company. Since then, however, 52 per cent. of the revenues have been set aside for the plan organization for expenditure in its seven-year programme 1956–62. The

plan lists projects on which funds, presumed to be available,
are to be used.   Of the total plan expenditure of $1160 million,
of which 80 per cent. was to come from oil revenues, 22 per cent.
was to be spent on agriculture, 35 per cent. on transport,
18 per cent. on industries and mines, 14 per cent. on social
improvements and the remainder on administration and
training.

Expenditure on agriculture is largely concerned with
irrigation facilities—understandably in an area where rainfall
is unreliable and where the irrigated 15 per cent. of the
cultivated area produces over 50 per cent. of the total output.
Of the expenditure on transport 61 per cent. was set aside for
railway improvement projects.   The expenditure on industry
and mines is largely for the development of factories designed
to produce important consumer goods such as cement and
textiles.

Thus the use of oil revenues has been planned to bring about
quite fundamental developments in the economic structure of
Iran, and it has been argued that this is the most significant
aspect of the oil industry, 'which is in no sense [*sic*] indigenous
to the Iranian economy . . . and does not provide the nucleus
around which the economy can develop. . . . It does not,
therefore, play a "leading sector" role similar to that played
by the textile, iron and steel, railroad and automobile industries
in the earlier stages of the development of some of the western
nations.   The industry then is important in Iran's development
because it provides a source of easily controlled and easily
mobilized revenue for the government and a supply of foreign
exchange greatly in excess of what the "indigenous" Iranian
industries could possibly earn'.[31]

It is significant that the question has been raised whether
the money available from oil revenues can, in fact, be effectively
used.   It has been observed that 'the organization, managerial
and labour inputs available to match the financing ability are
inadequate' and that 'the economy is extremely rigid and
unresponsive with social arrangements deeply engrained in the
society that are the virtual antithesis of those required to
facilitate economic growth'.[32]   An example of this is found in
the general land use and tenure system, which is an obstacle
to the effective use of irrigation water from the oil-revenue

financed multi-purpose dams. The validity of the economic arguments to support this view can be recognized, but it has also been argued that these do not perhaps take fully into account the fact that the implementation of the projects can perhaps be the greatest single factor in overcoming the difficulties encountered and 'thus the effects of the plan will be reflected more in the essential qualitative changes in the economy, rather than in the usual measures of economic performance. . . . The use of oil revenues to contribute to this purpose rests, therefore, on the same justification as their use to achieve a given rate of increase in *per capita* income'.[33] In either case, however, the impact of the use of the oil revenues on the economic and social geography of Iran will be readily apparent.

In the small oil-producing states of the Persian Gulf the use of the oil revenues for economic development is limited by aridity and by the absence of other important natural resources. Moreover, the need for such development is minimized by the small numbers of inhabitants for whom, unlike Iraq and Iran, unemployment and under-employment is not a major problem.

Kuwait, with revenues approaching $400 million a year * for a population of only 320,000, allocates about 20 per cent. to an investment fund to safeguard the country's future financial position. The one-third of the revenues allocated to development have largely been spent on the social services— housing, education and the medical services—but much capital has been invested in the search for water and in the provision of large-scale sea water distillation plants. An irrigation scheme based on the new availability of water is under consideration. Transport facilities—roads, seaports and airports —have been improved and state oil revenue has also been used to stimulate industrial development. For example, a state controlled brick works, a cement works and a chlorine factory are in production and a plant to manufacture asbestos pipe and sheet is under construction.[34] In Kuwait, however, it is opportunity rather than capital that is in short supply, and possibilities are being examined for making some of the

* There is the prospect of a much higher income within a few years if the Shell off-shore concession produces oil and when the areas of the country given up by the Kuwait Oil Company in 1962 are reallocated to other companies which may be expected to seek oil there as quickly as possible.

P

surplus capital available for development projects in other parts of the Middle East where oil revenues are insufficient to provide needed development capital. In 1961, Kuwait established a £50 million fund as the first stage in this process and loans, each of about £7 million, have been extended to the Sudan and to Jordan to help finance the foreign exchange costs of some of their development projects.

Thus the impact on economic development of the oil revenues paid to the producing countries has started to transgress national boundaries and add a further element to the international character of the oil industry.

REFERENCES

1 R. C. Estall and R. O. Buchanan. *Industrial Activity and Economic Geography*, 1961, pp. 60–61.

2 S. H. Longrigg. *Oil in the Middle East*, 2nd Edition, 1961, pp. 99, 106, 229.

3 W. E. Pratt. *Oil in the Earth*, 1942, p. 31.

4 Sheik A. Tariki. 'Natural Gas in the Middle East.' Paper delivered to the Arab Oil Congress. Alexandria. October 1961.

5 International Bank for Reconstruction and Development, *The Economic Development of Venezuela*, 1961, pp. 226–232.

6 For a consideration of these see United Nations *The Economic Development of Latin America and its Principal Problems*. An essay by Dr. Raul Prebisch, Secretary General of the U.N. Economic Commission for Latin America. 1950.

7 *Petroleo Inter-Americano*. December 1960, p. 40.

8 Preston E. James. *Latin America*. pp. 63–64.

9 Gilbert J. Butland. *Latin America. A Regional Geography*, pp. 147–149.

10 S. H. Longrigg. *Op. cit.*, pp. 101, 135, 217, 312.

11 *Ibid.*, p. 19.

12 *Ibid.*, pp. 19–20.

13 L. Lockhart. *Persian Cities*, 1960, pp. 162–164.

14 *Petroleum Press Service*, 'The Agglomeration of Abadan', February 1960, p. 55.

15 Information from a private report on Abadan prepared in Iran and made available to the author.

16 *Petroleum Press Service*. Op. cit., p. 55.

17 Report on Abadan. *Op. Cit.*

18 Shell International Petroleum Company, *The Economic Impact of Oil Operations in Producing Countries*, 1959, pp. 12–13.

19 S. H. Longrigg. *Op. cit.*, p. 133.

20 N. Bodington. *The Awakening Sahara*, 1961, p. 193.

21 Shell International Petroleum Company. *Op. cit.*, p. 5.

22 Edwin Lieuwen. *Venezuela*, R.I.I.A., 1962, p. 117.

23 *Ibid.*, p. 149.

24 G. Lenczowski. *Oil and State in the Middle East*, 1960, p. 68.

25 W. Jablonski. 'The Kuwait Off-shore Concession.' *Petroleum Week*, 6th January 1961, p. 16.

26 Edwin Lieuwen. *Op. cit.*, p. 113.

27 *Ibid.*, p. 55.

28 *Ibid.*, p. 64.

29 International Bank for Reconstruction and Development, *The Economic Development of Venezuela*, 1961.

30 S. H. Longrigg. *Op. cit.*, p. 214.

31 H. J. Bruton. 'Notes on Development in Iran.' *Economic Development and Cultural Change.*   Vol. IX, No. 4, Part I, July 1961, p. 627.

32 H. J. Bruton. *Ibid.*, p. 639.

33 H. J. Bruton. *Ibid.*, pp. 639–640.

34 *Petroleum Press Service.*   'Kuwait branches out', July 1961, pp. 246–247.

APPENDIX

Notes on Measurement in the Oil Industry

1. In general throughout this book quantities of oil have been expressed in *Metric Tons*. (A metric ton with 2204·6 lbs. is slightly smaller than an English Ton of 2240 lbs. and rather larger than a Short Ton with 2000 lbs.)

2. Quantities of oil are measured in different ways in different parts of the world. In the United States of America and in those countries where U.S. companies have been largely responsible for the development of the oil industry, the unit of measurement is the *Barrel*. (This consists of 42 American gallons equal to approximately 35 Imperial gallons). Quantities may thus be expressed in the number of barrels (abbreviated to bbls.) but, more often, the quantities produced or refined, etc., are also related to time and expressed as so many *Barrels per Day* (abbreviated to b/d). The relationship between tons and barrels is shown below.

In certain other countries the unit of measure is the *Cubic Metre* (*e.g.* Argentina) or the *Kilolitre* (*e.g.* Japan). These may as an approximation be equated with a metric ton.

In other parts of the world (notably the Soviet Union and the United Kingdom) and in the publication of most international organizations quantities of oil are expressed in terms of its weight. *Metric Tons* are most often used but *English Tons* are occasionally employed.

3. The relationship between the weight of a liquid and its cubic measure depends on its specific gravity. As crude oils and oil products vary in their specific gravities (see page 31) it is not therefore possible to give a single conversion factor which can be invariably applied. However, the following

table is a rough guide to the relationship between metric tons and barrels.

Barrels per Metric Ton

Gasolines	8·1 to 9·0
Kerosenes	7·6 to 8·2
Gas/Diesel Oils	6·9 to 7·8
Fuel Oils	6·5 to 6·9

Crude Oils vary between 6·5 and 8·2 barrels per metric ton but as most of the commoner crudes have an A.P.I. Gravity (see note on page 31) of between 27 and 35 degrees, it is possible, as a rule of thumb, to convert metric tons to barrels by multiplying by 7·5.

4. The factor for converting metric tons per year into barrels per day also depends on the specific gravity. However, the following method is often used to secure an approximate answer—

Metric Tons per Year ÷ 50 = Barrels per Day

Examples:

(*a*) Annual production of 4,500,000 metric tons from an oilfield can be expressed as a production of 4,500,000 ÷ 50 = 90,000 b/d.

(*b*) A refinery can be said to have a capacity of 650,000 metric tons per annum or of 650,000 ÷ 50 = 13,000 b/d.

For converting refining capacity from tons to b/d it is convenient to remember that 1 million tons per year = 20,000 b/d.

Index